DINOSAURS
of the World

with an Introduction by
Mark Norell

American Museum of Natural History
Co-curator, Halls of Dinosaurs and Hall of Vertebrate Origins

Consultants
Michael Benton

Professor of Vertebrate Paleontology, University of Bristol
Codirector, The Dinosaur Society

Tom Holtz

Assistant Research Scientist and Lecturer in Vertebrate Paleontology,
Department of Geology, University of Maryland

Edited by
Chris Marshall

1

Abelisaurus - Arrhinoceratops

Marshall Cavendish
New York . London . Toronto . Sydney

Marshall Cavendish Corporation
99 White Plains Road
Tarrytown, New York 10591-9001

Printed and bound in Italy

Library of Congress Cataloging-in-Publication Data

Dinosaurs of the world / with an introduction by Mark Norell ;
  consultants, Michael Benton, Tom Holtz ; edited by Chris Marshall.
    p. cm.
    Includes bibliographical references and index.
    Contents: 1. Abelisaurus–Arrhinoceratops — 2. Avialans
–Chasmosaurus — 3. Chialingosaurus–Diplodocus — 4. Dromaeosaurs
–Geological time — 5. Giganotosaurus–Kentrosaurus — 6. Kritosaurus
–Nodosaurus — 7. Omeisaurus–Plants — 8. Plateosaurus–Sauropelta —
9. Sauropodomorph dinosaurs–Syntarsus — 10. Talarurus
–Zephyrosaurus — 11. Index.
    ISBN 0-7614-7072-7 (set : lib. bdg. : acid-free paper)
    1. Dinosaurs—Encyclopedias, Juvenile. 2. Paleontology—
  Encyclopedias, Juvenile. [1. Dinosaurs—Encyclopedias.
  2. Paleontology—Encyclopedias.]   I. Marshall, Chris. II. Marshall
  Cavendish Corporation.
  OE862.D5D524   1998
  567.9'03—DC21
                                                    97–43365
                                                        CIP
                                                        AC

ISBN 0-7614-7072-7 (set)
ISBN 0-7614-7073-5 (vol. 1)

Picture credits
Color illustrations: Arril Johnson 22–23, 32, 34–35; Steve Kirk 14–15, 16–17, 24–25, 30–31, 38–39, 42–43, 48–49, 62–63; James G. Robins 12–13, 40–41, 50–51, 52–53, 60–61; Steve White 18–19, 20–21, 28–29, 44–45, 46, 56–57.
Photographs: Lynda Richardson/Corbis 6; Sovrintendenza Beni Archeologici Salerno 7; ©Kennan Ward Photography/Corbis 28; Michael Fogden & Patricia Fogden/Corbis 36; Joe McDonald/Corbis 54.

BROWN PARTWORKS

Editor: Chris Marshall
Assistant editors: Shona Grimbly, Alex MacKenzie, Matthew Turner, Clint Twist
Art editors: Steve Wilson, Graham Curd
Picture researcher: Brigitte Arora
Color illustrations: Arril Johnson, Steve Kirk, James G. Robins, Steve White (all of The Dinosaur Society Artists' Guild)
Line art and silhouettes: Guy Smith, Mainline Design; Denise Blagden and David Nicholls©Salamander Picture Library
Maps and family trees:
Colin Woodman
Authors: Paul Barrett (University of Cambridge), Donald Henderson (University of Bristol), Tom Holtz (University of Maryland), James I. Kirkland (Dinamation International Society), Mark Norell (American Museum of Natural History). With additional material by Liz Cook, David Gower, Jo Wright (all of the University of Bristol).

MARSHALL CAVENDISH CORPORATION

Editorial director: Paul Bernabeo
Project editor: Debra M. Jacobs

The Consultants
Michael Benton is Professor of Vertebrate Paleontology at the University of Bristol. He has a Ph. D. from the University of Newcastle and has had a research career of over 20 years. He works on the origin of the dinosaurs and other animals of the Triassic period. He has published 30 books, from popular works about dinosaurs and prehistoric life to basic textbooks on paleontology.

Tom Holtz is an Assistant Research Scientist and Lecturer at the University of Maryland, College Park. He has a Ph. D. from Yale University and specializes in theropod evolution. He works on the origin and behavior of *Tyrannosaurus* and other tyrannosaurs. He has published many articles and technical papers on dinosaurs and has taken part in dinosaur documentaries in the US and overseas.

Contents

articles on ornithischian dinosaurs   articles on saurischian dinosaurs   articles on general topics

Set Contents

■ articles on ornithischian dinosaurs   ■ articles on saurischian dinosaurs   ■ articles on general topics

INTRODUCTION
Dinosaur Science Today

by Mark Norell
American Museum of Natural History

Most people think that dinosaurs are extinct. Most believe that all dinosaurs were huge, simple-minded, mostly vicious lizards. Others picture dinosaurs battling each other, terrorizing cave dwellers, destroying cities with radiation breath, or anesthetizing children with insipid songs. Hopefully, what you read in this encyclopedia will change all that.

Dinosaur paleontologists have made a lot of progress in the last 20 years. We are living during a renaissance in dinosaur science.

Formerly a backwater of scientific credibility, the study of dinosaurs has taken center stage in the vertebrate paleontology community. The story of this renaissance has two parts.

One part concerns the animals, represented by fossils. Lots of new dinosaurs have been found recently and are continuing to be found. These new animals have been discovered by

▼ How many dinosaurs can you see in this picture? According to some scientists, pigeons, and all modern birds, are dinosaurs.

international teams of dinosaur hunters scouring the globe for new animal species. The result of this effort has been an onslaught of some great—and some not-so-great—discoveries littering the pages of newspapers worldwide. Just 10 years ago we knew nothing about *Eoraptor*, *Scipionyx*, *Mononykus*, *Giganotosaurus*, *Deltadromeus*, *Argentinosaurus*, *Unenlagia*, or *Sinraptor*, to name only a few.

The second part of the story of dinosaur science today concerns the result of all this dinosaur collecting. The way in which dinosaur scientists evaluate their evidence has been fundamentally changed.

Previously, determining how dinosaurs were related to one another, what they ate, or how they behaved was based largely on experience. Different specialists carved out niches; if you were interested in a particular topic you just sought out the right expert, who would provide an answer based on his or her own experience.

Now it is a different game: there is a premium on evidence. It is no longer important what famous scientists believe. Now they need to prove their ideas with rigorous, repeatable analyses and a lot of very convincing data. Consequently, we have learned more about dinosaurs in the last 20 years than in all the time they had been known previously. This growth of knowledge is particularly evident if you compare this encyclopedia with books that were written 25 years ago.

Perhaps the most surprising and controversial advancement in knowledge concerns increasing evidence that dinosaurs are not extinct. Look closely at a pigeon, or dissect your next roasted turkey. Both these animals and their closest Mesozoic relatives have a number of features in common. Modern birds and advanced nonavian theropods share characteristics such as a wishbone and an S-shaped neck. Both walk with their backbones parallel to the ground, and, at least primitively, both have three fingers and three primary toes that point forward.

▲ The Early Cretaceous Italian dinosaur *Scipionyx* was named in 1998. At about 9 in (25 cm) long, it is one of the smallest dinosaurs ever found and was probably a juvenile. It is also the only dinosaur to be found with some internal organs preserved.

Spectacular new fossils from China show that at least some prehistoric animals had fluffy body coverings. Some even had feathers. In Mongolia we find evidence that nonavian dinosaurs sat on their nests, brooding their eggs in the same posture that modern birds use today. These discoveries demonstrate that the nonavian dinosaurs were even more birdlike than we ever could have imagined. If we could transport ourselves back to Cretaceous Mongolia, when birds' closest relatives, such as dromaeosaurs, oviraptors, and troodontids, abounded, I am confident that we would look at these animals, compare them with birds, and conclude that there is no difference.

Many scientists are still trying to answer the question: What killed the dinosaurs? One reply is: Which dinosaurs?, because evidence is mounting that some dinosaurs survived. We just call them birds. In the pages that follow we explore details about the long-departed relatives of birds: how they lived, what they looked like, where they are found, and what kinds of plants and other animals lived with them. These are the concerns that occupy a creative group of scientists that is bringing the past to life, arranged here from A to Z for your enjoyment.

How to Use this Set

These two pages explain how to use our 11-volume set, *Dinosaurs of the World*. Volumes 1 to 10 contain more than 200 articles on dinosaurs, groups of dinosaurs, animals that lived alongside the dinosaurs, and other dinosaur-related topics. Volume 11 contains reference information, maps, and indexes.

Dinosaurs of the World is arranged in alphabetical order. Each entry is two to four pages long and contains a number of different items.

At the start of each entry are the title and a brief description of the dinosaur. Beneath the summary, the main text begins. Prepared by paleontologists, the dinosaur entries explain where and when the dinosaur was found, what type of dinosaur it was, what other dinosaurs it was related to, what it ate, and evidence for how it might have lived.

The central feature of each dinosaur entry is the color illustration, showing the animal as it might have looked when it was alive. Longer entries have extra photographs of recent finds, of paleontologists working in the field, and of modern animals that may have similar habits or features to the dinosaurs.

Extra details about the dinosaurs and their world are provided in fascinating facts boxes. An information panel lists vital statistics such as when and where an animal lived. To find out more, a Check These Out! box guides you to other related articles in the set.

title

Rhabdodon

Rhabdodon was a medium-sized plant-eating dinosaur that lived in Europe at the end of the Cretaceous period. It might have been the last iguanodontid dinosaur (*Iguanodon* relative) to walk the earth.

summary

Rhabdodon was first described in 1869 by the French paleontologist Philippe Matheron from a few fragments of leg, jaw, and back bones found in southern France. He was able to identify the remains as those of an ornithopod (bird-footed dinosaur). Other incomplete remains were later found in Austria, Spain, and Romania.

Classifying *Rhabdodon*
Rhabdodon's large leg bones and small arm bones indicate that it mostly walked on two legs. Some features of its jaw, such as parallel rows of teeth and the absence of teeth at the front of the upper jaw, suggest that *Rhabdodon* belonged to the

fascinating facts box

ISLAND DINOSAUR

Paleontologists believe that the evolutionary line leading to *Rhabdodon* began at about the time of the split between the iguanodontids and the hypsilophodontids in the Late Jurassic period (about 175 million years ago). *Rhabdodon*'s ancestors seem to have evolved separately from other ornithopods. Perhaps its ancestors became separated from environments in which more advanced (highly evolved) ornithopods, such as the hadrosaurs (duckbill dinosaurs) of North America and China, developed.

About 70 million years ago, during the Late Cretaceous period, much of Europe was a series of islands. The bones of various small dinosaurs have been found preserved in the rocks deposited as sediments on or near these islands. *Rhabdodon* was one of these dinosaurs. Many of the dinosaurs are primitive (little evolved) for the Late Cretaceous, which suggests they might have evolved in isolation, much like the marsupials (pouched mammals) of Australia.

color artwork

iguanodontids (a group of plant-eating dinosaurs named in honor of *Iguanodon*). However, other jaw features, such as teeth with ridges running from the edges to the base, were like those of the hypsilophodontids (a group of

main text

▶ *Rhabdodon* was a small ornithopod (bird-footed dinosaur) similar overall to *Camptosaurus*.

494

caption

Color artwork

The color artwork shows how our team of paleontologists and artists believe the dinosaur might have looked. Dinosaur colors are very controversial. After all, it is impossible to tell that a zebra has stripes just by looking at its skeleton.

photographs

pronunciation

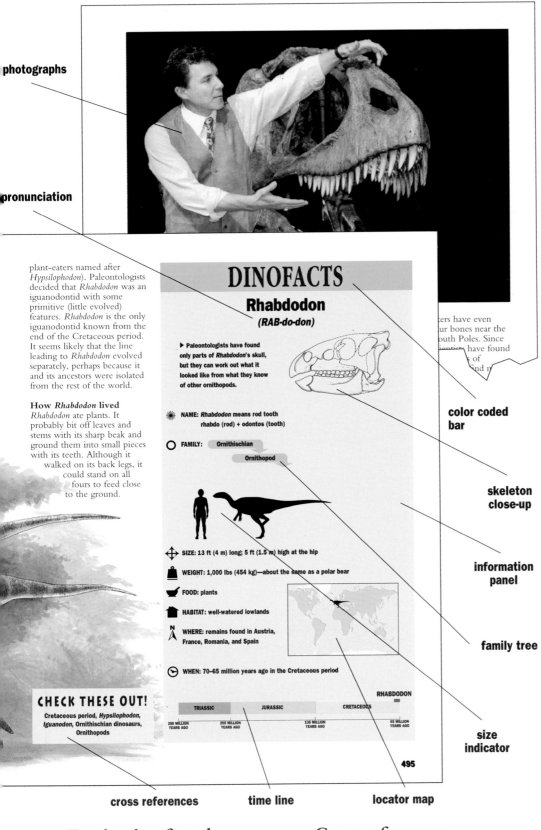

plant-eaters named after *Hypsilophodon*). Paleontologists decided that *Rhabdodon* was an iguanodontid with some primitive (little evolved) features. *Rhabdodon* is the only iguanodontid known from the end of the Cretaceous period. It seems likely that the line leading to *Rhabdodon* evolved separately, perhaps because it and its ancestors were isolated from the rest of the world.

How *Rhabdodon* lived
Rhabdodon ate plants. It probably bit off leaves and stems with its sharp beak and ground them into small pieces with its teeth. Although it walked on its back legs, it could stand on all fours to feed close to the ground.

CHECK THESE OUT!
Cretaceous period, *Hypsilophodon*, *Iguanodon*, Ornithischian dinosaurs, Ornithopods

DINOFACTS

Rhabdodon
(RAB-do-don)

▶ Paleontologists have found only parts of *Rhabdodon*'s skull, but they can work out what it looked like from what they know of other ornithopods.

✳ NAME: *Rhabdodon* means rod tooth
rhabdo (rod) + odontos (tooth)

○ FAMILY: Ornithischian
Ornithopod

✛ SIZE: 13 ft (4 m) long; 5 ft (1.5 m) high at the hip

⚖ WEIGHT: 1,000 lbs (454 kg)—about the same as a polar bear

🍃 FOOD: plants

⛰ HABITAT: well-watered lowlands

🧭 WHERE: remains found in Austria, France, Romania, and Spain

🕐 WHEN: 70–65 million years ago in the Cretaceous period

RHABDODON

TRIASSIC	JURASSIC	CRETACEOUS	
250 MILLION YEARS AGO	205 MILLION YEARS AGO	135 MILLION YEARS AGO	65 MILLION YEARS AGO

...ters have even ...ur bones near the ...outh Poles. Since ...have found ...of ...nd...

color coded bar

skeleton close-up

information panel

family tree

size indicator

495

cross references   **time line**   **locator map**

Photographs
Four-page entries and general entries are illustrated with photographs to show how paleontologists work today.

Information panel
An information panel gives the dinosaur's vital statistics, such as how big it was and what it weighed, what its name means, what it ate, and in what sort of terrain it lived.

Color coded bar
An at-a-glance guide to the subject: purple for saurischian dinosaurs; yellow for ornithischians; blue for other animals and general topics.

Skeleton close-up
These drawings show parts of the dinosaur's skeleton in greater detail.

Family tree
Each dinosaur entry has a small family tree showing the dinosaur's ancestry. Larger trees are found at the front of each volume and in the index volume.

Size indicator
Each entry on an individual dinosaur compares the dinosaur's size to a 6 ft (1.8 m) person. Very small animals are shown alongside a house cat.

Locator map
A colorful map shows where the animal's fossil remains were discovered.

Time line
The time line shows when the animal lived.

Fascinating facts box
Informative boxes provide background about the dinosaur and its world, and compare the dinosaur to modern animals.

Cross references
This box helps you to find out more by listing the articles in the set that are related to the entry you have just read.

9

The tree of life

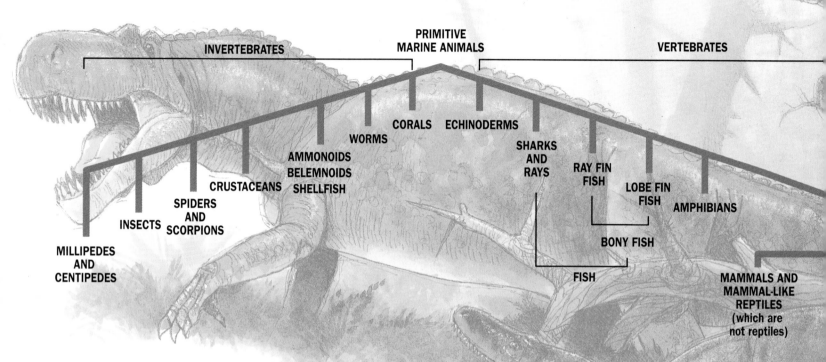

INVERTEBRATES | PRIMITIVE MARINE ANIMALS | VERTEBRATES

CORALS ECHINODERMS

WORMS

SHARKS AND RAYS

RAY FIN FISH

AMMONOIDS BELEMNOIDS SHELLFISH

CRUSTACEANS

LOBE FIN FISH

AMPHIBIANS

SPIDERS AND SCORPIONS

INSECTS

BONY FISH

MILLIPEDES AND CENTIPEDES

FISH

MAMMALS AND MAMMAL-LIKE REPTILES (which are not reptiles)

The history of life looks a bit like an upside-down tree. A common ancestor at the top diverges into different branches, and these branches into even more branches, and so on. The branches represent different groups of life-forms.

Scientists seek to understand just how this tree grew and how life-forms are related to one another. One of their methods is to identify special features. Every living thing has its own unique mix of features, for example, types of bones or numbers of fingers. Some features will be new (they have evolved on their own), and some features will be old (they were inherited from ancestors). By studying these features, or traits, we can climb backward

on the tree of life to find out how different kinds of living things are related.

Let's start with birds. If you examined a bird's skeleton, you would find that it has a flexible neck joint. The first theropod (two-legged meat-eating dinosaur) also had a flexible neck joint. In our tree of life, a group of organisms includes the common ancestor and all of its descendants. For example, the theropod group includes the first theropod and all of its descendants, so scientists identify our bird as a theropod. The bird has a long neck that it inherited from the first saurischian dinosaur, so the bird is also considered a saurischian dinosaur. The bird's hip sockets allow it to walk

with its legs held beneath its body. It inherited these hips from the first dinosaur, so our bird is also considered to be a dinosaur. The holes in its skull in front of its eye sockets came from the first archosaur, so we group it as an archosaur. Our bird has scales around its feet, which it inherited from its reptile ancestors, so it is also part of the reptile branch of the tree of life. Our bird has a backbone inside its body, so, like mammals, amphibians, and fish, it is also a vertebrate.

This diagram shows how groups of animals are linked. By following the tree upward from birds or from any group of animals, you can find out how the different groups of animals are related.

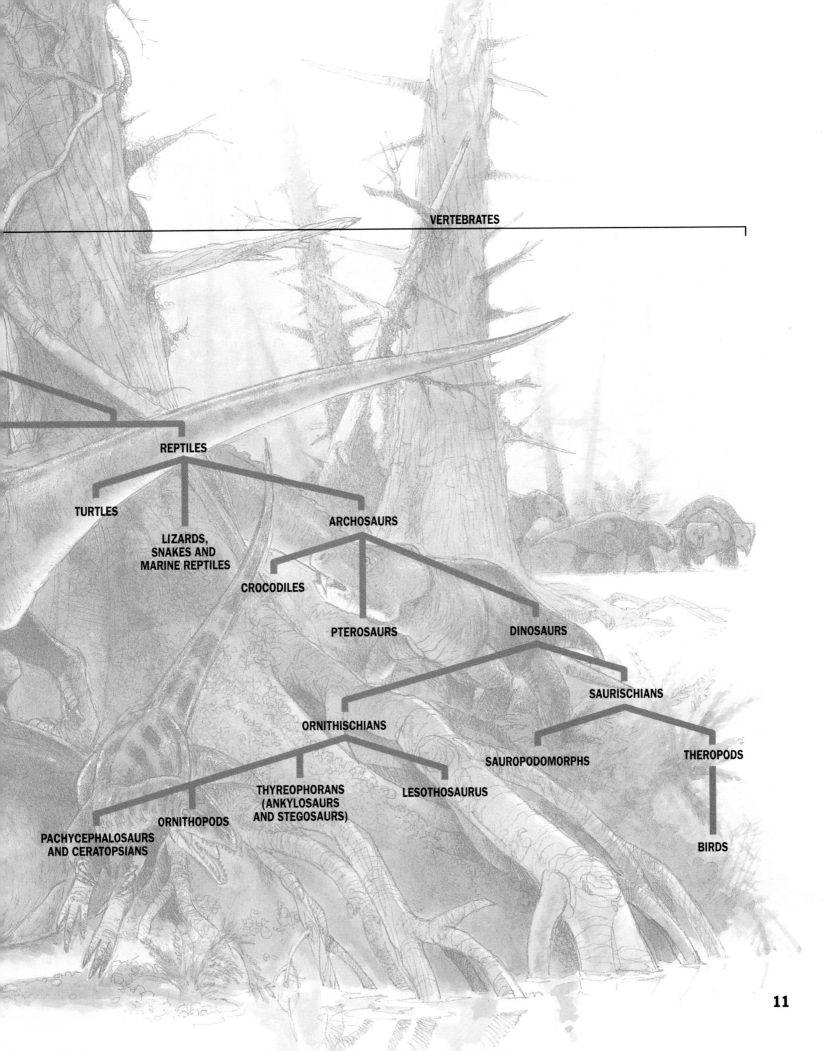

VERTEBRATES

REPTILES

TURTLES

LIZARDS,
SNAKES AND
MARINE REPTILES

ARCHOSAURS

CROCODILES

PTEROSAURS

DINOSAURS

SAURISCHIANS

ORNITHISCHIANS

SAUROPODOMORPHS

THEROPODS

THYREOPHORANS
(ANKYLOSAURS
AND STEGOSAURS)

LESOTHOSAURUS

ORNITHOPODS

PACHYCEPHALOSAURS
AND CERATOPSIANS

BIRDS

Abelisaurus

Abelisaurus was a large theropod (two-legged meat-eater) that lived in Argentina. It has given its name to a group of dinosaur predators that ruled the southern hemisphere in the Cretaceous period.

In the 1980s, the skull of a Cretaceous theropod was found in Argentina. The skull was 34 in (86 cm) long with powerful teeth. This was clearly the remains of a very large predator.

OTHER ABELISAURS

Abelisaurus and *Carnotaurus* were the first two abelisaurs recognized by paleontologists, but others are now known. Some, like *Xenotarsosaurus* and *Noasaurus*, also lived in South America. Others such as *Indosaurus* and *Indosuchus* lived in India, while *Majungatholus* (formerly known as *Majungasaurus*) hunted in Madagascar. Recent discoveries of more complete skeletons of *Majungatholus* and *Xenotarsosaurus* will allow scientists to discover what features were shared by all abelisaurs, and which were unique to particular kinds.

Abel's dinosaur

Argentine paleontologists José Bonaparte and Fernando Novas described and named the new dinosaur. In honor of its discoverer, Roberto Abel, they called it *Abelisaurus*.

Abelisaurus's skull had many interesting features. It was very tall and deep, with a ridge of bone over each eye, rather similar to the tyrannosaurs (two-fingered meat-eaters)

▶ *Abelisaurus* probably hunted young sauropods in the forests of Cretaceous South America.

Tyrannosaurus and *Tarbosaurus*. However, *Abelisaurus* was clearly different from the tyrannosaurs in other details of the back and sides of its skull.

The nearest relative that the paleontologists could identify was *Carnotaurus*, which was also from Argentina, but was almost 25 million years older! *Carnotaurus* belonged to the ceratosaurs, a group of four-fingered theropods that also included *Ceratosaurus*, *Coelophysis*, and *Dilophosaurus*.

Because *Abelisaurus* and *Carnotaurus* were more similar to each other than to any other ceratosaur, Bonaparte and Novas placed them in their own group within the ceratosaurs, the abelisaurs. Other abelisaurs were soon discovered in India and in Madagascar, an island off the east coast of Africa.

Top predator
Abelisaurus lived in the last part of the Cretaceous period, at the same time as tyrannosaurs were hunting duckbill and horned dinosaurs in North America and Asia. South of the equator, the abelisaurs hunted sauropods and other plant-eaters, but no one hunted them.

CHECK THESE OUT!

Carnotaurus, Ceratosaurs, Coelophysis, Cretaceous period, Dilophosaurus, Majungatholus, Saurischian dinosaurs, Tyrannosaurs

DINOFACTS

Abelisaurus
(ah-BELL-ih-SORE-us)

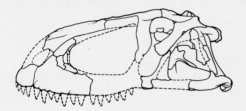

▶ Fossil-hunters have found only *Abelisaurus*'s skull. However, the powerful teeth tell them that this was a meat-eating dinosaur.

✳ **NAME:** *Abelisaurus* means Abel's lizard
Abel (Roberto Abel, discoverer of the fossil) + sauros (lizard)

○ **FAMILY:**

Saurischian
Theropod
Ceratosaur

✛ **SIZE:** about 33 ft (10 m) long; about 8 ft (2.4 m) high at the hip

⚖ **WEIGHT:** about 2.5 tons (2.2 tonnes)—about the same as 10 tigers

🥣 **FOOD:** meat

🏠 **HABITAT:** forests

🧭 **WHERE:** remains found in Argentina

🕐 **WHEN:** 71–68 million years ago in the Cretaceous period

			ABELISAURUS
TRIASSIC	JURASSIC	CRETACEOUS	
250 MILLION YEARS AGO	205 MILLION YEARS AGO	135 MILLION YEARS AGO	65 MILLION YEARS AGO

Acrocanthosaurus

Acrocanthosaurus was the biggest predator of the mid–Cretaceous period in North America. It is known from skeletons, teeth, and a set of tracks that may show it hunting sauropods.

In the United States, dinosaurs from both the Late Jurassic period (155–135 million years ago) and from the end of the Late Cretaceous period (80–65 million years ago) have been known for over 100 years. However, very little was known about US dinosaurs between these periods.

The bones of the biggest predator to roam North America between Late Jurassic

ON THE TRACK OF A SAUROPOD

In the early 1940s, American paleontologist Roland T. Bird reported a trackway from the Paluxy River of Texas. These tracks, which were the same age as the rocks in which *Acrocanthosaurus* was found, contained the footprints of a large sauropod (long-necked plant-eater), perhaps a relative of *Brachiosaurus*, and a large theropod. The theropod tracks, which are the right size and shape to have been made by *Acrocanthosaurus*, follow the sauropod tracks.

At one point, the theropod trail shows two right footprints without a left footprint in between. Bird thought that this meant that the theropod (*Acrocanthosaurus*) had grabbed on to the sauropod with its foot in an attack. Because the trackways may not be exact or complete, it is hard to tell precisely what happened 100 million years ago.

Allosaurus and Late Cretaceous *Tyrannosaurus* were discovered in the 1940s. In Oklahoma and Texas, fossil-hunters found the remains of two big theropods (two-legged meat-eaters) in rocks of the mid-Cretaceous period.

US paleontologists J. Willis Stovall and Wann Langston Jr. described this new theropod in 1950. A giant relative of the three-fingered meat-eater

▶ *Acrocanthosaurus*'s tall spines would have been covered with skin, giving the dinosaur a ridged back when it was alive.

14

Allosaurus, it mostly resembled that earlier, smaller theropod. However, this new find had tall spines on its neck, back, hip, and tail bones. Because of these spines, Stovall and Langston named it *Acrocanthosaurus*, tall-spined lizard.

For many years, these two skeletons were the only known remains of *Acrocanthosaurus*. Then in Texas and Oklahoma, fossil-hunters found more specimens. In Utah and Maryland, teeth and bones belonging to *Acrocanthosaurus* or to a very similar dinosaur were found. It seems likely that *Acrocanthosaurus* lived across much of North America in the mid-Cretaceous period.

How did it live?

Acrocanthosaurus was a *Tyrannosaurus*-sized hunter. In its shadow lived the dromaeosaur (clawed meat-eater) *Deinonychus*.

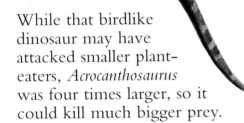

While that birdlike dinosaur may have attacked smaller plant-eaters, *Acrocanthosaurus* was four times larger, so it could kill much bigger prey.

CHECK THESE OUT!

Allosaurus, Brachiosaurus, Cretaceous period, Deinonychus, Footprints, Saurischian dinosaurs, Theropods, Tyrannosaurus

DINOFACTS

Acrocanthosaurus
(AH-crow-CAN-thuh-SORE-us)

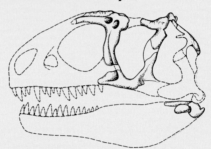

▶ Only fragments of *Acrocanthosaurus*'s skull have been found. Paleontologists think it was fairly like *Allosaurus*'s skull but without the crests in front of the eyes.

✳ **NAME:** *Acrocanthosaurus* means tall-spined lizard
acro (tall) + akantha (spine) + sauros (lizard)

○ **FAMILY:**   Saurischian
  Theropod
  Tetanuran

✛ **SIZE:** about 40 ft (12.2 m) long; up to 10 ft (3 m) high at the hip

WEIGHT: up to 4.5 tons (4 tonnes)—about the same as 9–10 polar bears

FOOD: meat

HABITAT: varied, from dry uplands to sea coastlines

N **WHERE:** remains found in what is now Oklahoma, Texas, Utah, and possibly Maryland

🕐 **WHEN:** 115–105 million years ago in the Cretaceous period

			ACROCANTHOSAURUS
TRIASSIC	JURASSIC	CRETACEOUS	
250 MILLION YEARS AGO	205 MILLION YEARS AGO	135 MILLION YEARS AGO	65 MILLION YEARS AGO

Afrovenator

Afrovenator was a general purpose meat-eater that lived in Africa in the Cretaceous period. Even though it had no special features, it is important in understanding the history of African dinosaurs.

In 1990, US paleontologist Paul Sereno joined the British Museum of Natural History on a dinosaur hunt in Africa. While in the desert country of Niger, Sereno spotted a row of bones from a sauropod (long-necked plant-eater) at a location called In Abaka. He could not recover the bones on that expedition, so he made plans to return to Niger.

In 1994, Sereno led an international team of paleontologists and geologists back to In Abaka. There the team found and uncovered the remains of an Early Cretaceous sauropod, which has yet to be officially named or described.

They also found the remains of a new theropod (two-legged meat-eater). Like most meat-eaters, it had bladelike, serrated teeth and large, grasping hands.

SAHARAN DINOSAURS

Besides *Afrovenator*, fossil-hunters have found the remains of other dinosaurs in the Sahara Desert. These include the mid-Cretaceous theropods *Carcharodontosaurus* and *Spinosaurus*, both of them giants. Smaller than these was the sail-backed plant-eater *Ouranosaurus*. A few sauropods (long-necked plant-eaters) have also been discovered in North Africa, but their remains were not very complete. Alongside these dinosaurs lived turtles and huge, 50 ft (15.2 m) crocodiles.

▶ *Afrovenator* hunted in the forests of Early Cretaceous Africa. Along with an unnamed sauropod, it is the earliest dinosaur that fossil-hunters have found in the Sahara Desert.

Because it had three fingers, all of its teeth in front of its eye sockets, and stiffening structures in its tail, Sereno knew that it was a tetanuran (stiff-tailed meat-eater).

African hunter

This was a new theropod, unlike any other known from Africa. The team named it *Afrovenator*, the African hunter. At 27 ft (8.2 m) long, it was not amazingly big. It did not have huge claws or tall spines, and it was not a specialized runner. It was a fairly primitive (little evolved), general purpose tetanuran.

What was important was *Afrovenator*'s age. By comparing the animals and plants found with it to similar fossils from other parts of the world, the scientists figured out that it was from the Early Cretaceous. No dinosaurs had previously been known in all of Africa between the Late Jurassic and the mid-Cretaceous periods, but now two had been found: the sauropod and *Afrovenator*. From these and other remains found in the late 1990s, Sereno and his team are trying to piece together African dinosaur history between the Late Jurassic and the mid-Cretaceous periods.

How did *Afrovenator* live?

Afrovenator was a hunter that roamed what is now one of the largest deserts on earth. In *Afrovenator*'s day the Sahara was covered in forests and rivers. *Afrovenator* probably used its powerful hands to hold onto its victim, while it slashed out lumps of meat with its teeth.

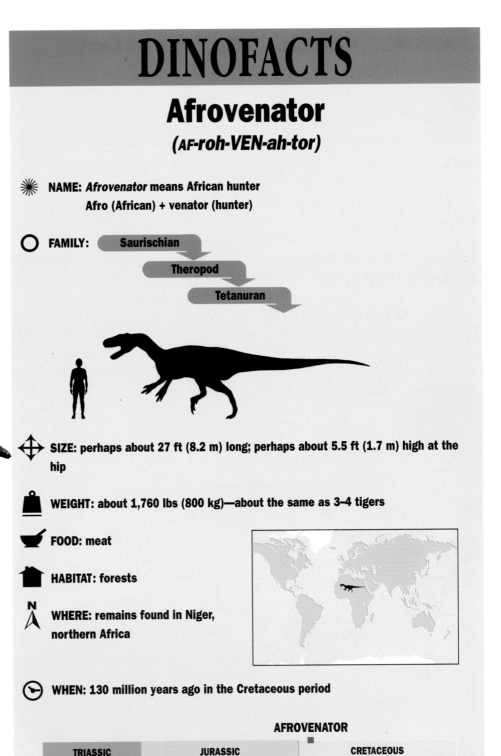

DINOFACTS

Afrovenator
(AF-roh-VEN-ah-tor)

✳ **NAME:** *Afrovenator* means African hunter
Afro (African) + venator (hunter)

◯ **FAMILY:** Saurischian → Theropod → Tetanuran

✛ **SIZE:** perhaps about 27 ft (8.2 m) long; perhaps about 5.5 ft (1.7 m) high at the hip

WEIGHT: about 1,760 lbs (800 kg)—about the same as 3–4 tigers

FOOD: meat

HABITAT: forests

WHERE: remains found in Niger, northern Africa

WHEN: 130 million years ago in the Cretaceous period

		AFROVENATOR	
TRIASSIC	JURASSIC		CRETACEOUS
250 MILLION YEARS AGO	205 MILLION YEARS AGO	135 MILLION YEARS AGO	65 MILLION YEARS AGO

CHECK THESE OUT!

Carcharodontosaurus, Cretaceous period, *Ouranosaurus*, *Spinosaurus*, Tetanurans, Theropods

Alamosaurus

Alamosaurus was one of the last of the sauropods (long-necked plant-eating dinosaurs). It lived at the very end of the Cretaceous period, and was one of the very last dinosaurs to walk the earth.

Alamosaurus was the last of the titanosaurs (armored sauropods). Titanosaurs were a group of primitive (little evolved) sauropods that survived long after most other sauropods had become extinct. They included *Antarctosaurus, Argentinosaurus, Hypselosaurus,* and *Saltasaurus.*

WHERE THE SAUROPODS ARE

Sauropod footprints and bones are very common in Late Jurassic North American rocks. In the southern hemisphere, many armored sauropod (titanosaur) fossils have been found in later, Cretaceous period rocks. What story do these fossils tell?

Did the sauropods migrate south? Did the sauropods become extinct in Cretaceous North America? Perhaps they died out due to a changing climate, or increased competition for food. Now paleontologists have found *Alamosaurus* in North America at the end of the Cretaceous period. How does this change the story? We would need a lot more evidence to know what happened to the northern sauropods.

▼ *Alamosaurus* steers clear of *Quetzalcoatlus,* a huge pterosaur (flying reptile) that lived in North America in the Late Cretaceous period.

US paleontologist Charles W. Gilmore first discovered *Alamosaurus* in Texas in 1922. Fossil-hunters have since found more remains in Texas, New Mexico, and Utah. They do not have a complete *Alamosaurus* skeleton to study, though: only parts of hips, a tail, a shoulder blade, a front leg and foot, some chest bones, and a few teeth. From these remains, though, they can tell that *Alamosaurus* was pretty big.

Weighty problem

At about 48 ft (14.5 m) long, *Alamosaurus* was large for a titanosaur. Most titanosaurs were about three-quarters its size. Many other kinds of sauropods that grew to great size (for example, *Apatosaurus* and *Diplodocus*) had weight-saving hollows on the sides of each backbone. However, titanosaurs evolved without these hollows. Because most titanosaurs never grew more than about 38 ft (11.6 m) long, body weight was not a serious problem for them.

How *Alamosaurus* lived

No head has yet been found for *Alamosaurus*. Sauropod heads were fairly small and fragile compared to the total size of the dinosaur and were easily crushed and lost after the dinosaur died. However, we can assume that *Alamosaurus* ate plants, as all sauropods did. The size of *Alamosaurus*'s bulky body tells us it held the large guts it needed to break down the food that it swallowed whole.

Like *Titanosaurus*, another titanosaur, *Alamosaurus* probably had small armor plates set in its skin. Fossil-hunters have not yet found any *Alamosaurus* armor, though.

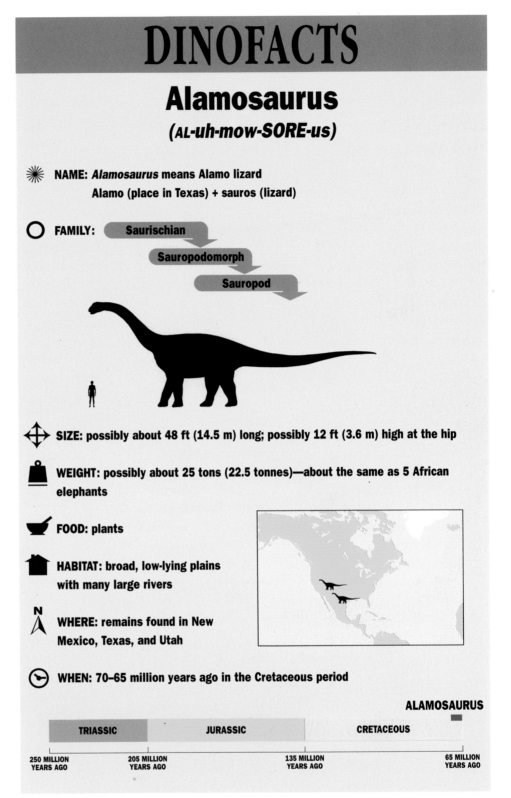

DINOFACTS

Alamosaurus
(AL-*uh-mow*-SORE-*us*)

✳ **NAME:** *Alamosaurus* means Alamo lizard
Alamo (place in Texas) + sauros (lizard)

⦿ **FAMILY:** Saurischian → Sauropodomorph → Sauropod

✛ **SIZE:** possibly about 48 ft (14.5 m) long; possibly 12 ft (3.6 m) high at the hip

WEIGHT: possibly about 25 tons (22.5 tonnes)—about the same as 5 African elephants

FOOD: plants

HABITAT: broad, low-lying plains with many large rivers

WHERE: remains found in New Mexico, Texas, and Utah

🕑 **WHEN:** 70–65 million years ago in the Cretaceous period

TRIASSIC	JURASSIC	CRETACEOUS	ALAMOSAURUS
250 MILLION YEARS AGO	205 MILLION YEARS AGO	135 MILLION YEARS AGO	65 MILLION YEARS AGO

CHECK THESE OUT!
Argentinosaurus, Pterosaurs, *Saltasaurus*, Sauropods, *Titanosaurus*

Albertosaurus

Albertosaurus was one of North America's most common tyrannosaurs (two-fingered meat-eaters), but was *Albertosaurus* just one kind of tyrannosaur or two kinds? Scientists are not sure.

In the late 1800s, the Geological Survey of Canada brought back many fossils from the badlands of western Canada. Among the fossils they found were two skulls belonging to large theropod (two-legged meat-eating) dinosaurs. US paleontologist E. D. Cope and Canadian paleontologist Lawrence M. Lambe thought they both belonged to the theropod "Laelaps" (now called *Dryptosaurus*) that Cope had discovered.

Meanwhile, Henry Fairfield Osborn of the American Museum of Natural History in New York City was studying a new giant theropod, which he called *Tyrannosaurus rex*. Osborn recognized that the Canadian dinosaurs were not *Dryptosaurus* but relatives of *Tyrannosaurus*. In 1905, Osborn named the Canadian dinosaur *Albertosaurus* in honor of Alberta, where it was found.

Enter *Gorgosaurus*
Then in the summer of 1913, Canadian fossil-hunter Charles H. Sternberg came across an

▲ Like other tyrannosaurs, big-headed *Albertosaurus* probably attacked its prey with its huge jaws and teeth.

ALBERTOSAURUS VS. GORGOSAURUS

Lawrence M. Lambe believed that *Albertosaurus* and *Gorgosaurus* were two different types of tyrannosaurs, and for many years paleontologists agreed with him. Then in 1970, Canadian theropod expert Dale A. Russell suggested that *Albertosaurus* and *Gorgosaurus* were just two different kinds (species) of the same tyrannosaur. He pointed out that they were more similar to each other than to other tyrannosaurs. Most paleontologists accepted this and stopped using the name *Gorgosaurus*.

New evidence in the 1990s, however, showed that *Albertosaurus* and *Gorgosaurus* were as different from each other as from other tyrannosaurs. Some theropod experts said this meant that the two were really completely different tyrannosaurs and the name *Gorgosaurus* should be restored. They say that many museum displays of *Albertosaurus* should really be called *Gorgosaurus*.

almost complete tyrannosaur skeleton near the Red Deer River in Alberta. The rocks in which he found it were a little older than those in which the original *Albertosaurus* skulls were discovered. Lawrence M. Lambe studied it and noticed that the dinosaur's hand had only two fingers. Until then, paleontologists had assumed that tyrannosaurs had three, like *Allosaurus*. After discovering many more fossils, scientists have found that, like *Albertosaurus*, all tyrannosaurs had only two fingers.

Lambe thought this second skeleton was too old to be *Albertosaurus*, so he named it *Gorgosaurus*. Some paleontologists, however, believe that *Gorgosaurus* is just a different kind (species) of *Albertosaurus*.

How *Albertosaurus* lived
Albertosaurus was a smaller version of *Tyrannosaurus*. Its long, slender legs and shock-absorbing feet would have allowed it to outrun its prey: mainly the hadrosaurs (duckbill dinosaurs) and ceratopsians (horned dinosaurs), which were the most common large plant-eaters of its time.

CHECK THESE OUT!

Allosaurus, Cretaceous period, Saurischian dinosaurs, Theropods, Tyrannosaurs, *Tyrannosaurus*

DINOFACTS

Albertosaurus
(al-BER-tuh-SORE-us)

▶ *Albertosaurus*'s massive skull had openings, or windows, in front of the eye sockets. These openings would have made *Albertosaurus*'s head lighter and easier to move without making it any weaker.

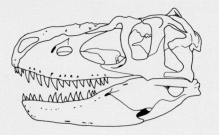

✳ **NAME:** *Albertosaurus* means Alberta lizard
Alberta (province of Canada) + sauros (lizard)

○ **FAMILY:** Saurischian → Theropod → Tyrannosaur

✛ **SIZE:** about 28 ft (8.5 m) long; about 9.25 ft (2.8 m) high at the hip

⚖ **WEIGHT:** about 2.75 tons (2.5 tonnes)—about the same as 6 polar bears

⌇ **FOOD:** meat

⌂ **HABITAT:** forests, uplands, riverbanks

N ↑ **WHERE:** remains found in the western United States and in Canada

⏱ **WHEN:** 80–68 million years ago in the Cretaceous period

			ALBERTOSAURUS
TRIASSIC	JURASSIC	CRETACEOUS	
250 MILLION YEARS AGO	205 MILLION YEARS AGO	135 MILLION YEARS AGO	65 MILLION YEARS AGO

Alectrosaurus

Alectrosaurus is one of the oldest known tyrannosaurs (two-fingered meat-eaters). For many years its bones were mixed up with the bones of another dinosaur, so nobody knew what it was.

Most tyrannosaurs, including *Albertosaurus, Daspletosaurus,* and *Tyrannosaurus* of North America and *Tarbosaurus* of Asia, were very similar. They had powerful skulls, long, slender legs, very short arms, and hands with only two fingers.

All the most famous tyrant dinosaurs lived in the last part of the Late Cretaceous period. In 1923, paleontologists from the American Museum of Natural History discovered the remains of an earlier tyrannosaur in Mongolia.

An odd-looking tyrant
George Olsen and Walter Granger first found some leg, arm, and hip bones. Later, about 100 ft (30 m) away, they found some more arm bones and some tail bones. Granger thought that all the bones belonged to the same dinosaur.

Back in New York, in 1933, paleontologist Charles Gilmore closely examined the bones. He saw that the first bones found were clearly from a tyrannosaur. However, some of the bones found in the second batch of fossils were unusual for a tyrannosaur. The arm bones were larger than those of a typical tyrannosaur, and the finger claws were huge.

▼ *Alectrosaurus* had long, slim legs, so it could probably run fast to catch its prey.

A BEAST WITH SIX HORNS

Another small tyrannosaur found in Mongolia was called *Alioramus*. This was younger than *Alectrosaurus*, and was found in rocks of the same age as those that contained the fossils of *Tarbosaurus*. *Alioramus* is known only from its skull and foot bones. Like *Alectrosaurus*, it had a long, tapered snout. Unlike the older dinosaur, however, *Alioramus* had a row of six bumps or small horns along the top of its snout. Because they would have been too small to be useful weapons, *Alioramus* probably just used its horny bumps for display. *Alioramus* was probably a little longer than *Alectrosaurus*. Its name means other branch because it was thought to represent a separate branch of the tyrannosaur family tree.

Gilmore named this new dinosaur *Alectrosaurus* (the unmarried dinosaur) because it was separate from the rest of the tyrannosaur group.

Mixed-up bones

Many decades later, Mongolian paleontologists discovered new specimens of *Alectrosaurus* that included the dinosaur's skull. Because *Alectrosaurus* was older than most tyrannosaurs, it reveals clues about the tyrannosaurs' ancestors. For example, *Alectrosaurus*'s skull was longer and its snout was more tapered than those of typical tyrannosaurs. American paleontologists then restudied the original *Alectrosaurus* fossils and decided that the arm bones with the huge claws were not from *Alectrosaurus* at all, but from one of the bizarre-looking therizinosaurs like *Segnosaurus* and *Erlikosaurus*.

How did *Alectrosaurus* live?

Like later tyrannosaurs, *Alectrosaurus* ran fast and ate meat. However, like primitive (less evolved) theropods, this early tyrannosaur had a delicate skull and thin teeth. It probably fed by neatly slicing chunks of meat rather than by pulling and tearing as did *Tyrannosaurus* and *Daspletosaurus*.

CHECK THESE OUT!

Cretaceous period, *Daspletosaurus*, *Erlikosaurus*, *Segnosaurus*, Tyrannosaurs

Alectrosaurus
(a-LECK-truh-SORE-us)

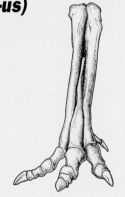

▶ Like other tyrannosaurs, *Alectrosaurus* had a powerful foot with three talons with which it could grab and hold down its prey.

✳ **NAME:** *Alectrosaurus* means unmarried lizard
alectros (unmarried) + sauros (lizard)

○ **FAMILY:** Saurischian

Theropod

Tyrannosaur

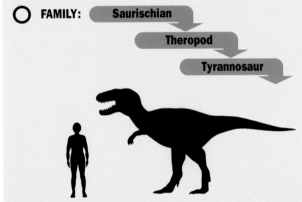

✥ **SIZE:** about 16 ft (5 m) long; about 4 ft (1.2 m) high at the hip

WEIGHT: about 700 lbs (320 kg)—about the size of a large grizzly bear

FOOD: meat

HABITAT: varied, from forests to lake shores to river valleys to dry regions

WHERE: remains found in Mongolia and China

🕐 **WHEN:** 75–73 million years ago in the Cretaceous period

ALECTROSAURUS

TRIASSIC	JURASSIC	CRETACEOUS
250 MILLION YEARS AGO	205 MILLION YEARS AGO	135 MILLION YEARS AGO · 65 MILLION YEARS AGO

Allosaurus

Allosaurus is the most common and the best known meat-eating dinosaur from the Late Jurassic period. It was a large, fierce predator with eagle-like talons, strong jaws, and fearsome teeth.

The Morrison Formation in the western United States is a series of rock layers stretching from Montana to New Mexico. These rocks are richer in dinosaur skeletons than any other Jurassic rocks.

Morrison dinosaurs

The most common Morrison dinosaurs are the sauropods (long-necked plant-eaters), such as *Apatosaurus, Brachiosaurus,* and *Camarasaurus.* Many ornithischians (bird-hipped plant-eaters) have also been found, such as plate-backed *Stegosaurus* and the ornithopod (bird-footed dinosaur) *Camptosaurus.*

Theropods (two-legged meat-eaters) are rarer. Morrison theropods include horned *Ceratosaurus* and birdlike *Ornitholestes*; however, by far the most common and best known of the Morrison predators is *Allosaurus.*

A petrified horse hoof?

Geologist Ferdinand V. Hayden discovered the first fragment of *Allosaurus* in Colorado in 1869. This was a broken half of a backbone (vertebra), which was jokingly called a petrified horse hoof because of its shape (petrified means turned to stone). This vertebra was described in 1873 by paleontologist Joseph Leidy, who named the fossil *Antrodemus.*

In 1877, paleontologist Othniel C. Marsh's team found a series of theropod bones in the Garden Park quarry of Colorado. They found vertebrae, foot and toe bones, fragments of arm bones, and teeth.

The vertebrae were hourglass shaped rather than spool shaped. Because they were clearly different from any of the other dinosaurs found in the quarry, Marsh named the new creature *Allosaurus*, the strange, or other, lizard.

Complete skeleton

Marsh's team found many more bones of *Allosaurus.* M. P. Felch recovered the best skeleton in Canyon City, Colorado, in 1883, after a year of digging. His find enabled paleontologists to study almost every part of *Allosaurus*'s skeleton. They discovered that this dinosaur, like most theropods, had bladelike, serrated teeth, powerful three-

▶ Large numbers of the fierce meat-eater *Allosaurus* roamed the western United States in the Late Jurassic period.

ALLOSAURUS AROUND THE WORLD?

There have been reports of *Allosaurus* remains discovered outside the Morrison Formation in the US, in places as far away as Africa, Siberia, Japan, and Australia. It is possible that *Allosaurus* did live in some other parts of the world during the Late Jurassic period. Some of the other Morrison dinosaurs, such as *Dryosaurus*, *Brachiosaurus*, and *Camptosaurus*, have been found in eastern Africa and Europe as well as western North America. Perhaps *Allosaurus* lived in these regions as well.

However, none of the reports of *Allosaurus* remains found outside the United States have been based on fossils that could come only from that dinosaur. Reports based on teeth or a bone or two could refer to many other sorts of tetanurans (stiff-tailed meat-eaters). Although it is possible that someday someone will find true *Allosaurus* remains in another country, for now it is just an American dinosaur.

fingered hands ending in eagle-like talons, strong three-toed feet, and a long tail. *Allosaurus* had a pair of small crests on its snout, and another pair just in front of its eyes.

Cleveland-Lloyd Quarry

After the turn of the century, many other museums began to discover *Allosaurus* specimens in Colorado, Wyoming, Montana, Oklahoma, and elsewhere. These ranged in size from small juveniles to giant adults, some possibly as big as *Tarbosaurus* or *Tyrannosaurus*.

Perhaps the most spectacular discovery was made in Utah, in what is now called the Cleveland-Lloyd Dinosaur Quarry. In 1927, Golden York, an assistant to University of Utah geologist Frederick Pack, found a treasure trove of over 800 dinosaur bones near the town of Cleveland.

Student paleontologist William Lee Stokes of Princeton University reopened the quarry in 1933. Over the next three years more than 1,500 bones were collected. Many years later, after Stokes had become head of the Department of Geology at the University of Utah, he began a new series of digs at the site. By the mid-1970s, thousands more bones had been found. Among these were the remains of at least 44, and possibly more than 50, different individuals of *Allosaurus*!

The typical tetanuran

Unlike most dinosaurs, which are known from incomplete fossils, *Allosaurus* is known from the entire skeleton. By examining its features, we can determine where it fits on the evolutionary tree of life.

Because it has an open hip socket and upright hind limbs that let it stand tall, we can tell that *Allosaurus* was a dinosaur.

In its hand, the second finger is the longest, the thumb claw is larger than the other claws, and the whole thumb sticks out at an angle: these features show that *Allosaurus* was a saurischian (lizard-hipped dinosaur).

As in all true theropods, only the middle three bones of the foot are used to support the creature's weight. The bone in front of the eye rises to the top of the skull (in *Allosaurus*, it supports a crest), and the dinosaur's teeth all lie in front of its eye socket. Its hand has only three fingers, and the tail has stiffening structures toward the back. These features show this dinosaur was a tetanuran (stiff-tailed meat-eater).

Close relations

Among the tetanurans are several other dinosaurs which seem to be closely related to *Allosaurus*. These include the earlier form *Cryolophosaurus*. They also include *Sinraptor*, which lived in China at the same time as *Allosaurus* lived in North America, and the later giants *Carcharodontosaurus*, *Giganotosaurus*, and *Acrocanthosaurus*. All these forms have extra openings in the nose bone and the upper jaw bone. They also have a modified bone at the back of the skull, where the neck joins the head.

All these dinosaurs can be grouped together and called the allosaurs, or three-fingered meat-eaters. Some paleontologists prefer to call these large meat-eaters carnosaurs.

Most paleontologists agree that these dinosaurs are more closely related to each other than to any other group of tetanurans, such as the tyrannosaurs (two-fingered tyrant dinosaurs), the ornithomimosaurs (ostrichlike dinosaurs), or the dromaeosaurs (clawed meat-eaters).

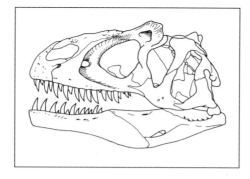

▲ *Allosaurus*'s skull was 3 ft (90 cm) long, and its powerful jaws contained more than 70 serrated teeth, each 3 in (7.6 cm) long.

Finding a wishbone

Scientists thought there was little to be learned from new skeletons of *Allosaurus*. However, even a dinosaur as well studied as *Allosaurus* can sometimes produce surprises. For example, in 1992, allosaur experts Daniel Chure and James Madsen reported that they had discovered a wishbone in *Allosaurus*.

A wishbone (or furcula) is formed when the collarbones of the shoulder join up and

▼ The sharp talons of a bald eagle grasp the top of a tree stump as the bird perches securely. The eagle's talons are remarkably similar to *Allosaurus*'s claws.

fuse together. Some birdlike theropods, such as *Oviraptor*, had wishbones, but this was the first time that an allosaur had been reported with a wishbone.

Why so sure?

Paleontologists could be sure they had discovered a wishbone in *Allosaurus* because they had a skeleton in which very few of the bones had been disturbed after death. Normally after an animal dies but before it gets buried there is some movement of the bones, by wind or water or scavenging animals. In this new specimen of *Allosaurus*, the wishbone was found in place: the shoulder part of the skeleton was still in the original position.

Not belly ribs

Now that they knew what an allosaur wishbone looked like, Chure and Madsen went back to study the *Allosaurus* remains found in the Cleveland-Lloyd Quarry. Among the many thousands of bones discovered in the quarry, they found many wishbones. These had previously been thought to be belly ribs, since paleontologists had not expected to find a wishbone in an allosaur.

The bird connection

Since that time wishbones have been found in many other tetanuran dinosaurs, including tyrannosaurs and dromaeosaurs. The presence of a wishbone in a tetanuran shows that birds are themselves just a specialized branch of the family tree of theropod dinosaurs.

How did *Allosaurus* live?

Allosaurus was without a doubt a meat-eater. It could run very fast on its powerful back legs. It had very large jaws lined with long, bladelike teeth. These would have been useless for grinding plants, but very effective for slicing out chunks of flesh from prey.

Allosaurus's arms were of medium length for a theropod, but very powerfully built, with large areas where arm muscles could attach. The claws are long and curved, and resemble the talons of an eagle. It is likely that these claws were specially adapted for holding squirming prey.

What did it eat?

It is unlikely that even the largest *Allosaurus* could attack an adult sauropod like *Brachiosaurus* or *Apatosaurus*, but it may very well have caught and eaten the young of these dinosaurs. Other, smaller victims may have included *Stegosaurus*, *Camptosaurus*, and the ornithopod *Dryosaurus*. Like most meat-eaters today, *Allosaurus* probably scavenged from any carcass it came across.

DINOFACTS

Allosaurus
(AH-*luh-SORE-us*)

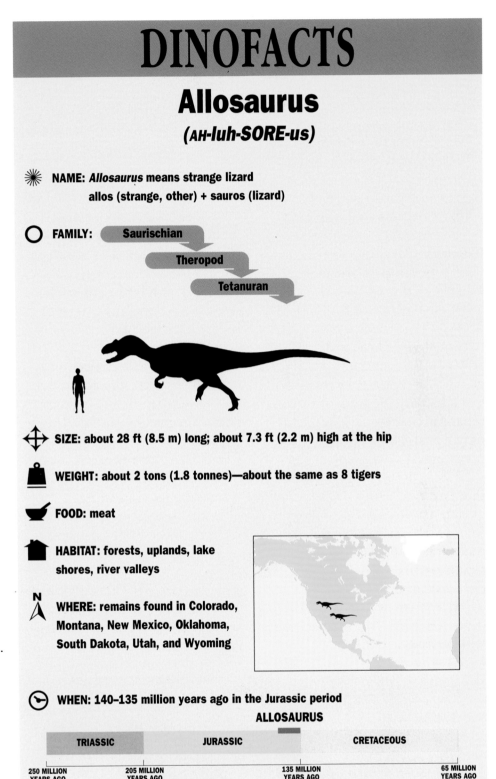

✳ **NAME:** *Allosaurus* means strange lizard
allos (strange, other) + sauros (lizard)

⚪ **FAMILY:** Saurischian → Theropod → Tetanuran

✛ **SIZE:** about 28 ft (8.5 m) long; about 7.3 ft (2.2 m) high at the hip

⚖ **WEIGHT:** about 2 tons (1.8 tonnes)—about the same as 8 tigers

FOOD: meat

🏠 **HABITAT:** forests, uplands, lake shores, river valleys

WHERE: remains found in Colorado, Montana, New Mexico, Oklahoma, South Dakota, Utah, and Wyoming

🕐 **WHEN:** 140–135 million years ago in the Jurassic period

	ALLOSAURUS	
TRIASSIC	JURASSIC	CRETACEOUS
250 MILLION YEARS AGO	205 MILLION YEARS AGO / 135 MILLION YEARS AGO	65 MILLION YEARS AGO

Alxasaurus

Alxasaurus is the oldest of the therizinosaurs, a group of bizarre-looking big-clawed dinosaurs. Its remains showed that therizinosaurs were plant-eating descendants of meat-eating dinosaurs!

In early fall 1988, Chinese and Canadian paleontologists discovered the remains of two individual specimens of a medium-sized dinosaur in Mongolia's Alxa Desert. There were enough bones to make one almost complete skeleton. However, no skull bones were found except a lower jaw.

The new dinosaur was named *Alxasaurus*. It had a long, slender neck, powerful arms with large claws, short, heavy legs, and a short tail.

The Alxa dinosaur

In Beijing, Chinese paleontologist Dong Zhiming and Canadian paleontologist Dale Russell identified *Alxasaurus* as a theropod (two-legged meat-eater). From the shapes of the back, arm, and hip bones, they could tell *Alxasaurus* was one of the odd-looking big-clawed therizinosaurs.

Alxasaurus was also the earliest known therizinosaur. It was found in rocks from the mid-Cretaceous period. Other therizinosaurs had been found only in Late Cretaceous rocks.

The teeth in *Alxasaurus*'s lower jaw were small and had rounded bumps. They were unlike the large, jagged-edged

▶ Like other therizinosaurs, *Alxasaurus* had a stockier body and shorter legs than most theropods. It also had fearsome-looking claws on its hands. However, this scary beast ate only plants.

ALXA'S RELATIVES

Alxasaurus was not the first therizinosaur to be discovered. During the 1970s and early 1980s, the remains of several smaller kinds, such as *Erlikosaurus* and *Segnosaurus*, had been found in Mongolia.

At first, paleontologists were unsure to which dinosaur group these specimens belonged. They were put into their own group, the segnosaurs (named for *Segnosaurus*). However, this did not solve the problem of how they fitted in with dinosaur classification. Because they had long necks and ate plants, some scientists thought that the segnosaurs were related to the prosauropods (early long-necked plant-eaters). The discovery of *Alxasaurus* enabled them to put it, and the segnosaurs, into a new group, the therizinosaurs.

teeth typical of theropods such as the tyrannosaurs. Because of the teeth, scientists decided that even though it belonged to the meat-eating theropods, *Alxasaurus* ate plants.

Study of *Alxasaurus*'s wrist showed that it was related to the maniraptors (long-armed meat-eaters). This meant that *Alxasaurus* was a plant-eater descended from meat-eaters.

How did *Alxasaurus* live?

Digesting plants requires a lot more intestines than digesting meat. Because of this, *Alxasaurus* had a wider body and shorter legs than most other theropods. It may have used its strong arms and claws to pull down branches so that it could feed, much as sloths do today. Its claws would also have been useful as defensive weapons.

DINOFACTS

Alxasaurus
(ALK-suh-SORE-us)

✳ **NAME:** *Alxasaurus* means Alxa lizard
Alxa (Alxa Desert, where it was found) + sauros (lizard)

◯ **FAMILY:**

Saurischian → Theropod → Tetanuran

✛ **SIZE:** about 12.5 ft (3.8 m) long; about 5 ft (1.5 m) high at the hip

⚖ **WEIGHT:** up to 850 lbs (385 kg)—about the same as a zebra

🥣 **FOOD:** plants

🏠 **HABITAT:** forests and lake shores

↑N **WHERE:** remains found in Mongolia

🕐 **WHEN:** 112–110 million years ago in the Cretaceous period

		ALXASAURUS	
TRIASSIC	JURASSIC		CRETACEOUS
250 MILLION YEARS AGO	205 MILLION YEARS AGO	135 MILLION YEARS AGO	65 MILLION YEARS AGO

CHECK THESE OUT!

Cretaceous period, *Erlikosaurus*, Prosauropods, Saurischian dinosaurs, *Segnosaurus*, Theropods, Tyrannosaurs

Amargasaurus

Amargasaurus was a sauropod (long-necked plant-eater) first found in Argentina in the late 20th century. It is remarkable for the long spines along its backbone, which would have looked like a mane.

Fossil-hunters found an almost complete *Amargasaurus* skeleton in La Amarga canyon of Argentina. Like *Dimetrodon* (a mammal-like reptile with a tall back sail), *Amargasaurus* had long spines running along the back of its neck and the top of its back. No one is sure what the spines did.

A colorful flag

Amargasaurus's spines would not have grown from the skin like those of stego-saurs (plate-backed dinosaurs). Instead, *Amargasaurus*'s spines were very long parts of its neck and back bones. All paleonto-logists agree that these long back spines were not for protection; they were too fragile. Perhaps *Amargasaurus* used the spines for display.

When the dinosaur was alive, the spines would have been covered over by skin. Perhaps the skin was brightly colored as well. Many modern lizards have brightly colored patches and frills under their chins. They nod their heads, or do push-ups with their arms. These signals warn off other lizards or attract mates. Perhaps *Amargasaurus* made signals by showing off its mane.

A SPINY STORY

Amargasaurus was a member of a small group of sauropods called the dicraeosaurids (two-spined lizards). These were related to the diplodocids—dinosaurs like *Diplodocus* and *Apatosaurus.* Both the diplodocids and the dicraeosaurids had very unusual neural spines. The neural spine is the flat bone that sticks up and slightly backward at the very top of every backbone. The diplodocids and dicraeosaurids had a neural spine that split down the middle so that from the front it looked like the letter U. A strong, elastic cable of tissue ran along the base of the U shape and helped to hold up the head and neck. Dicraeosaurids had longer neural spines than those of any diplodocid, and *Amargasaurus*'s neural spines were the longest of all.

How *Amargasaurus* lived

The teeth of *Amargasaurus* tell us that it ate plants. The mane on its neck suggests that *Amargasaurus* lived in groups or small herds. Only animals that live in herds or have territories have evolved such large display structures; think of the horns of deer and antelope, or of the bright colors of many birds.

Like all sauropods, *Amargasaurus* moved on all fours. It probably could not run fast. Small groups of *Amargasaurus* would have moved slowly across open forest areas, feeding on trees and bushes.

▼ *Amargasaurus* may have used its neck ridge to attract a mate or to send signals to other dinosaurs.

CHECK THESE OUT!

Apatosaurus, Cretaceous period, **Diplodocus**, Mammal-like reptiles, **Sauropods**

DINOFACTS

Amargasaurus
(ah-MAR-gah-SORE-us)

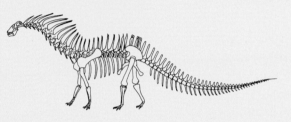

▶ The skeleton of *Amargasaurus* shows the very long spines along the neck, back, and tail.

✳ **NAME:** *Amargasaurus* means Amarga lizard
Amarga (canyon in Argentina) + sauros (lizard)

○ **FAMILY:** Saurischian
Sauropodomorph
Sauropod

✛ **SIZE:** 40–50 ft (12.2–15.2 m) long; 13 ft (4 m) high at the hip

⚖ **WEIGHT:** 10–20 tons (9–18 tonnes)—about the same as 2–4 African elephants

FOOD: plants

🏠 **HABITAT:** broad, forested river valleys

N **WHERE:** remains found in Argentina

🕐 **WHEN:** about 130–120 million years ago in the Cretaceous period

AMARGASAURUS

TRIASSIC	JURASSIC	CRETACEOUS
250 MILLION YEARS AGO	205 MILLION YEARS AGO	135 MILLION YEARS AGO	65 MILLION YEARS AGO

Ammonoids

Ammonoids are some of the most common fossils of the Mesozoic Era. Relatives of modern squid, but with a coiled outer shell, ammonoids swam in Mesozoic seas, hunting small marine animals.

The ammonoids died out with the nonflying dinosaurs, about 65 million years ago. Before this, they had a long history going back to about 375 million years ago. During that time, their shape changed little. The soft-bodied animals had tentacles around their mouth and lived inside a shell. They were related to other ancient sea creatures called belemnoids.

Today, the ammonoids' closest relative is the chambered nautilus of the Pacific and Indian oceans. Scientists think that the ammonoids and the nautilus may have descended from the same ancestors, the nautiloids, which evolved during the Silurian period 440–410 million years ago.

MOSASAUR BITES

Large ammonoid fossils are often found with mosasaur tooth marks in them. Mosasaurs were Cretaceous marine reptiles. University of Indiana paleontologist Erle Kauffman found that the tooth marks belonged to the mosasaur *Clidastes*. He also noted that the mosasaurs attacked in the same way. First, a mosasaur attacked the ammonoid from above and behind, puncturing the ammonoid's shell to sink it. Then it tried to swallow the ammonoid, which explains why small bitten ammonoid shells are not found: they were eaten. If the ammonoid was too big to swallow, the mosasaur kept biting until it could rip the ammonoid out of its shell.

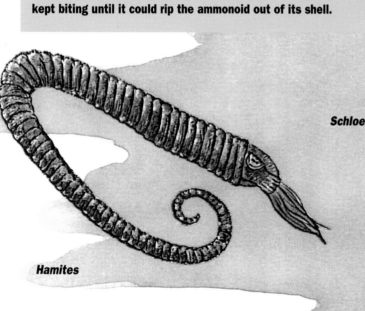

Schloenbachia

Hamites

▶ The shells of most ammonoids were tightly coiled like the shell of *Schloenbachia*. Other ammonoids, like *Hamites*, evolved straighter shells. Both lived in the Cretaceous period.

Buoyant swimmers

Like the modern nautilus, ammonoids' shells had sealed chambers containing air. These air chambers stopped the animal from sinking to the sea-floor. The walls between the air chambers were folded into complex patterns. Today, paleontologists use these patterns to identify the different kinds of ammonoids.

Like modern squid and the nautilus, adult ammonoids moved around by squirting out a jet of water. However, compared to fish and squid, they probably swam slowly.

Mesozoic timekeepers

The ammonoids nearly became extinct several times before their final disappearance at the end of the Cretaceous period. They almost vanished at the end of the Devonian period (360 million years ago), at the end of the Permian period (250 million years ago), and at the end of the Triassic period (205 million years ago). Each time they recovered with many new and varied kinds.

Animal groups that nearly become extinct often evolve very rapidly. New kinds of ammonoids developed and disappeared every few hundred thousand years. Because fossil ammonoids are so widespread, and because paleontologists know which kinds lived when, ammonoids can be used to date rocks.

How did ammonoids live?

Ammonoids swam and drifted in the Mesozoic oceans, feeding on a variety of slow-moving, fishy prey. Whereas today's nautilus has a sharp beak, most ammonoids had blunt jaws. These jaws show they could eat tough foods, such as shellfish, that needed to be crunched.

Because there were so many ammonoids, they were probably hunted by many animals, such as large fish, crabs, and marine reptiles, including ichthyosaurs. In any food chain, there are always many fewer hunters than hunted. Some ammonoids developed spines for defense.

FOSSIL FACTS

Ammonoids
(AM-muh-NOIDS)

 NAME: Ammonoid means coiled like a ram's horn (the shape reminded people of the coiled rams' horns on the head of the ancient Egyptian god Ammon)

 SIZE: coiled shells—wide variation from 0.5 in (1.25 cm) to 5.5 ft (1.7 m) across; straight shells—up to 6 ft (1.8 m) long

 WEIGHT: wide variation from 0.5 oz (15 g) to 200 lbs (91 kg)

 FOOD: worms, shrimps, smaller ammonoids, and sometimes small fish

 HABITAT: seas and oceans except very close to shore

 WHERE: remains found worldwide

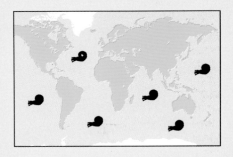

 WHEN: from 375 million years ago in the Devonian period to 65 million years ago in the Cretaceous period

AMMONOIDS

DEVONIAN	CARBONIFEROUS	PERMIAN	TRIASSIC	JURASSIC	CRETACEOUS
410 MILLION YEARS AGO	360 MILLION YEARS AGO	290 MILLION YEARS AGO · 250 MILLION YEARS AGO	205 MILLION YEARS AGO	135 MILLION YEARS AGO	65 MILLION YEARS AGO

CHECK THESE OUT!

Belemnoids, Cretaceous period, Extinction, Fish, Geological time, Mosasaurs, Shellfish, Triassic period

Amphibians

Today we have three main types of amphibians: jumping frogs and toads, crawling salamanders, and burrowing tropical blindworms. In the past, many large and exotic amphibians roamed the earth.

The word *amphibian* means an animal that lives a double life. This refers to amphibians' two-stage lifecycle. The first stage takes place entirely in water, while the second stage takes place mainly on land.

Most people are familiar with the transformation of small, swimming tadpoles into jumping frogs. Many other amphibians also go through this change.

Amphibians lay their eggs in water. Their young then hatch in water, and for a while they live like fish and breathe with gills. After a time, which can vary from a few days or weeks to even years, the bodies of these juveniles change. They develop legs, toes, lungs, and eyelids. Their internal organs change too.

Amphibians then move on to land for the second stage of their lives when they live as air-breathing, four-legged animals. When the land-living adults return to the water to lay their own eggs, the cycle starts again.

Land legs, water eggs

Amphibians include all the four-legged animals that do not lay their eggs on land. The legs of amphibians tell us that they are animals that have evolved to live on land. However,

because they have to return to water to breed, amphibians are not complete land-living animals like lizards or birds. Their eggs must develop and hatch near water, although they do not always have to remain underwater. Some can develop in moist surroundings. However, if the surrounding air or soil gets too dry the young amphibians inside the eggs will die.

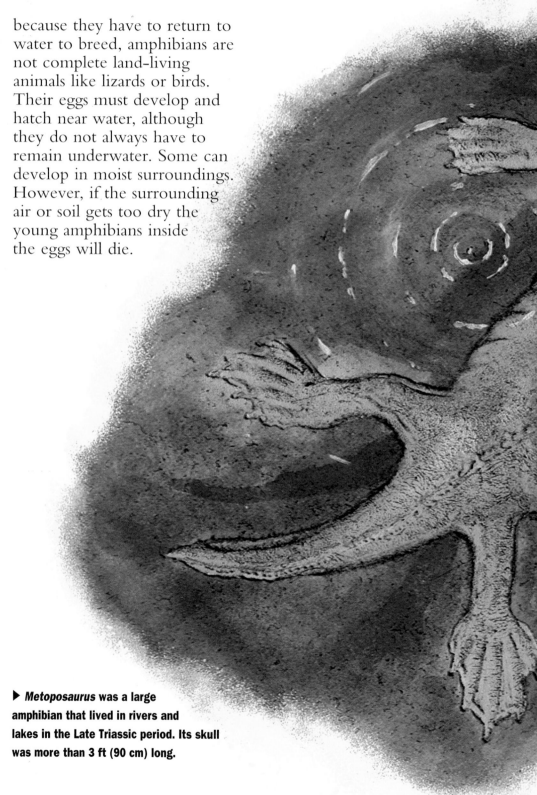

▶ *Metoposaurus* was a large amphibian that lived in rivers and lakes in the Late Triassic period. Its skull was more than 3 ft (90 cm) long.

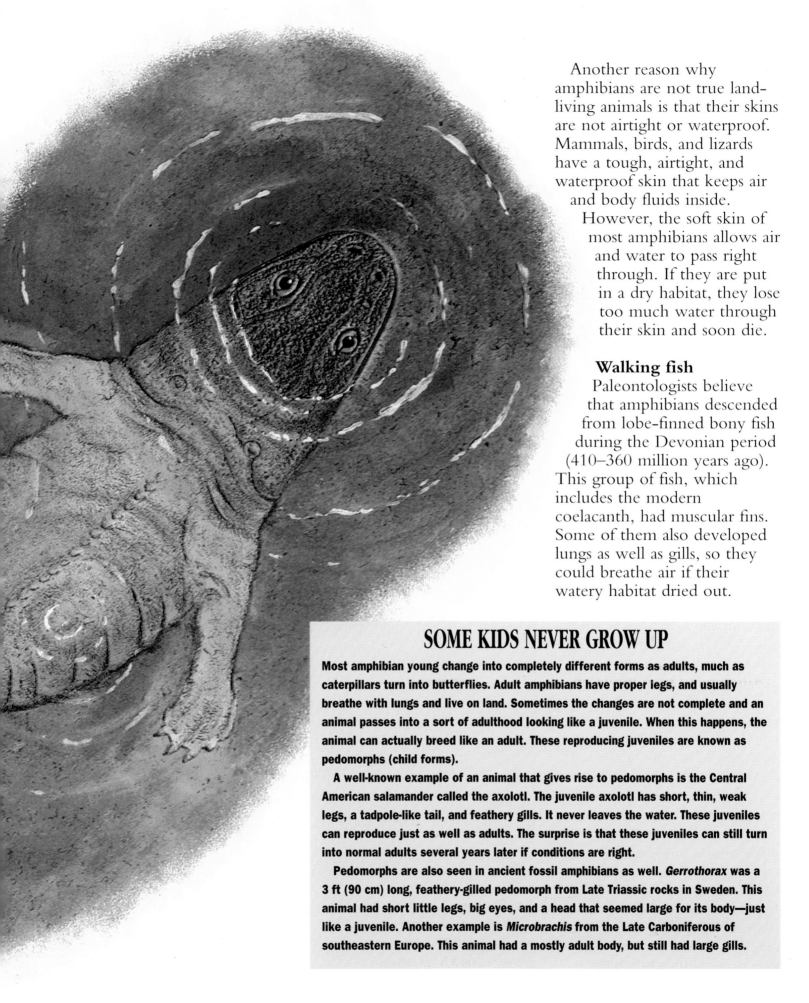

Another reason why amphibians are not true land-living animals is that their skins are not airtight or waterproof. Mammals, birds, and lizards have a tough, airtight, and waterproof skin that keeps air and body fluids inside.

However, the soft skin of most amphibians allows air and water to pass right through. If they are put in a dry habitat, they lose too much water through their skin and soon die.

Walking fish

Paleontologists believe that amphibians descended from lobe-finned bony fish during the Devonian period (410–360 million years ago). This group of fish, which includes the modern coelacanth, had muscular fins. Some of them also developed lungs as well as gills, so they could breathe air if their watery habitat dried out.

SOME KIDS NEVER GROW UP

Most amphibian young change into completely different forms as adults, much as caterpillars turn into butterflies. Adult amphibians have proper legs, and usually breathe with lungs and live on land. Sometimes the changes are not complete and an animal passes into a sort of adulthood looking like a juvenile. When this happens, the animal can actually breed like an adult. These reproducing juveniles are known as pedomorphs (child forms).

A well-known example of an animal that gives rise to pedomorphs is the Central American salamander called the axolotl. The juvenile axolotl has short, thin, weak legs, a tadpole-like tail, and feathery gills. It never leaves the water. These juveniles can reproduce just as well as adults. The surprise is that these juveniles can still turn into normal adults several years later if conditions are right.

Pedomorphs are also seen in ancient fossil amphibians as well. *Gerrothorax* was a 3 ft (90 cm) long, feathery-gilled pedomorph from Late Triassic rocks in Sweden. This animal had short little legs, big eyes, and a head that seemed large for its body—just like a juvenile. Another example is *Microbrachis* from the Late Carboniferous of southeastern Europe. This animal had a mostly adult body, but still had large gills.

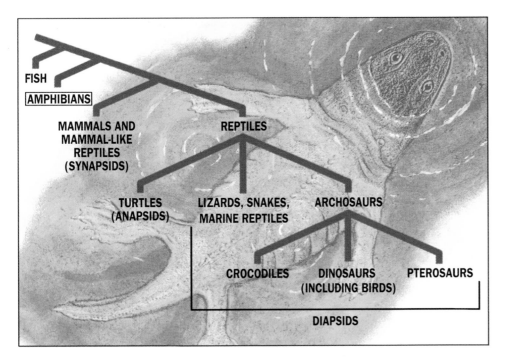

FISH
AMPHIBIANS

MAMMALS AND
MAMMAL-LIKE
REPTILES
(SYNAPSIDS)

REPTILES

TURTLES
(ANAPSIDS)

LIZARDS, SNAKES,
MARINE REPTILES

ARCHOSAURS

CROCODILES

DINOSAURS
(INCLUDING BIRDS)

PTEROSAURS

DIAPSIDS

◄ Amphibians, which are descended from fish, were the first four-legged animals. Amphibians belonging to one ancient group were the ancestors of the dinosaurs.

These two features, lungs and muscular fins, enabled amphibians to move out of the water and become the first land animals larger than insects. Their fins evolved into legs, and their lungs became larger and more efficient.

Early amphibians
The earliest known amphibians were *Ichthyostega* and *Acanthostega*, which lived at the end of the Devonian period. Paleontologists have found the remains of both animals in eastern Greenland.

These two amphibians were fairly alike, about 3 ft (90 cm) long with short, sturdy legs and small fins running along the tops and around the ends

of their tails. A complete skull has been found only for *Acanthostega*. The skull shows that this animal had a full set of gills and sharp, meat-eating teeth. Paleontologists believe that *Acanthostega* and *Ichthyostega* spent most of their time in water hunting for fish.

When on land, these early amphibians would have eaten worms and insects.

Amphibian explosion
During the Carboniferous period (360–290 million years ago), many different types of amphibians evolved. Some, such as *Eryops* from Texas and New Mexico, became large land-living predators. *Eryops* could grow up to 6.5 ft (2 m) long, and looked a lot like a modern alligator.

Other amphibians went back to living mostly in water. *Crassigyrinus*, from Scotland, had very small legs and could not possibly have moved about on land. It had large eyes and an enormous mouth. It seems that *Crassigyrinus* either lived in

▶ Amphibians have a double life: they begin life in water and then move onto land. This small, fishlike creature is a tree frog tadpole from Costa Rica in Central America. Like many juvenile amphibians, it looks nothing like the adult form that it will change into when it reaches maturity.

deep waters where the light was low, or hunted fish only during the night.

One important group of amphibians that appeared during the Carboniferous period were the anthracosaurs (coal lizards). They had many advanced (highly evolved) features, and are believed to be the ancestors of the reptiles.

Decline on land

During the Permian period (290–250 million years ago), amphibians began to spend less time on land. The reptiles and mammal-like reptiles were both better at being land animals, and the amphibians became mostly water animals.

One of the most unusual was *Diplocaulus* from Texas. This animal was about 3.3 ft (1 m) long and had a boomerang-shaped head that was four times wider than its body. Scientists think that by angling its head upward or downward, *Diplocaulus* could rise or dive through the water, in the same way that submarines use vanes.

Modern amphibians

Modern amphibians, such as frogs and salamanders, first appeared in the Mesozoic Era. The earliest known froglike animal was *Triadobatrachus*, which lived about 240 million years ago in the Triassic period in Madagascar.

Triadobatrachus was 4 in (10 cm) long and had a much longer back than modern frogs. Modern frogs have only 5–9 bones forming the spine, but *Triadobatrachus* had 24. The earliest known true frog,

Prosalirus, appeared about 190 million years ago in the Early Jurassic period. Fossil specimens have been found in Arizona.

The earliest known salamander is *Karaurus*. This lived in Kazakhstan about 150 million years ago in the Late Jurassic period.

The origin of tropical blindworms is still a mystery. There are very few fossils of these soft-bodied animals.

FOSSIL FACTS

Amphibians
(am-FIH-bee-anz)

✳ **NAME:** Amphibian means double life
amphi (double) + bios (life)

✦ **SIZE:** large variation from 2 in (5 cm) to 16 ft (5 m) long

WEIGHT: large variation from 4 oz (120 g) to 1,300 lbs (590 kg)

FOOD: insects, worms, fish, other amphibians

HABITAT: lakes, ponds, streams, swamps, and forests

WHERE: remains found worldwide

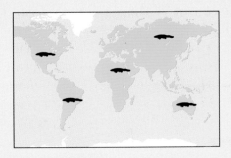

🕐 **WHEN:** from 370 million years ago in the Devonian period to today

REPTILES

DEVONIAN	CARBONIFEROUS	PERMIAN	TRIASSIC	JURASSIC	CRETACEOUS
410 MILLION YEARS AGO	360 MILLION YEARS AGO	290 MILLION YEARS AGO	250 MILLION YEARS AGO	205 MILLION YEARS AGO	135 MILLION YEARS AGO	65 MILLION YEARS AGO

CHECK THESE OUT!

Bony fish, Fossils, Geological time, Reptiles, Triassic period

Anatotitan

Anatotitan was a very large hadrosaur (duckbill dinosaur) with an amazingly long skull. It roamed the forests of Montana and South Dakota in the Late Cretaceous period.

The hadrosaurs were a group of ornithischian (bird-hipped) dinosaurs that evolved during the last part of the Cretaceous period. There were many kinds of hadrosaurs. *Anatotitan* was one of several types of very large, but rare, hadrosaurs.

Hadrosaurs are divided into two groups. The lambeosaurines (named for *Lambeosaurus*) had hollow crests; the hadrosaurines (named for *Hadrosaurus*) had small, solid crests or none at all. *Anatotitan* was a hadrosaurine.

Elongated skull

Anatotitan is known from one complete skull and three body skeletons. In 1975, paleontologist Michael Brett-Surman realized that most of the crestless duckbills that had been called *Anatosaurus* were really *Edmontosaurus*. However, one duckbill dinosaur was not like *Edmontosaurus* at all. Its skull was much too long and low. Its limbs were longer than those of

▶ With its wide mouth and strong jaw muscles, *Anatotitan* could munch its way through the toughest plants.

LARGE AND IN CHARGE

Scientists have learned that the amount of food an animal needs does not increase at the same rate as its body size. An elephant that is 1,000 times heavier than a rabbit does not need 1,000 times as much food. As an animal gets larger, the rate at which its body works gets slower. This means that large animals eat relatively less. The body of a tiny shrew works very fast, and this animal will die of starvation in less than a day if it does not eat. An elephant can go for several weeks without feeding.

It is thought that when plant-eating dinosaurs became large their bodies worked at a slower rate. This meant they could survive on much lower-quality plant food like ferns and pine needles. Perhaps being very large helped hadrosaurs like *Anatotitan* and *Edmontosaurus* survive in an increasingly crowded coastal environment.

Edmontosaurus, and it was the only hadrosaur to have teeth in less than half its jaw. In 1990, Brett-Surman named this dinosaur *Anatotitan*.

A wide mouth

All duckbill dinosaurs had a very wide snout that formed a shovel-shaped beak. Because of their wide mouths, the hadrosaurs could scoop up large mouthfuls of plants. Right behind their beaks were fleshy cheeks. *Anatotitan* would have snipped off leaves and stems with its beak, and chewed them up with its flat cheek teeth. Like other ornithopods (bird-footed dinosaurs), *Anatotitan* could swing its upper jaw outward like a hinge to grind its food efficiently.

How *Anatotitan* lived

Most paleontologists think that hadrosaurs lived in herds. Although there is no hard proof, scientists have found trackways that show a number of hadrosaurs moving in the same direction at the same time. Perhaps herds of *Anatotitan* slowly munched their way around the dense forests that covered much of their lowland habitat.

CHECK THESE OUT!

Cretaceous period, *Edmontosaurus*, Hadrosaurs, *Hadrosaurus*, *Lambeosaurus*, Ornithopods

DINOFACTS

Anatotitan
(ah-*NAH*-toe-*TIE*-tan)

▶ *Anatotitan*'s skull was almost 4 ft (1.2 m) long, longer than that of any other hadrosaur. It had no teeth in the front half of its jaws.

✳ **NAME:** *Anatotitan* means giant duck
anas (duck) + titan (giant)

○ **FAMILY:** Ornithischian
→ Ornithopod
→ Hadrosaur

✛ **SIZE:** about 38 ft (11.6 m) long; 14 ft (4.3 m) high at the hip

WEIGHT: 4–5 tons (3.6–4.5 tonnes)—about the same as 4–5 North American bison

FOOD: plants

HABITAT: coasts and forested lowland areas with rivers and lakes

WHERE: remains found in Montana and South Dakota

WHEN: 70–65 million years ago in the Cretaceous period

			ANATOTITAN
TRIASSIC	JURASSIC	CRETACEOUS	
250 MILLION YEARS AGO	205 MILLION YEARS AGO	135 MILLION YEARS AGO	65 MILLION YEARS AGO

Anchiceratops

Anchiceratops was a ceratopsian (horned dinosaur) that lived in North America in the Cretaceous period. As well as horns, *Anchiceratops* had a bony frill flaring upward and outward from the back of its head.

In 1912, US fossil-hunter Barnum Brown discovered part of a ceratopsian skull along the Red Deer River in Alberta, Canada. The fossil preserved all of the dinosaur's frill from the back edge to just in front of its eyes. Two years later, in 1914, Brown described the dinosaur. *Anchiceratops*'s frill was decorated with small triangle-shaped horns along the edge, so he named it *Anchiceratops ornatus* (decorated near to horn face).

Its large frill identified *Anchiceratops* as belonging to the chasmosaurine group of ceratopsians. The other main ceratopsian group, the centrosaurines, had smaller frills.

THE SECOND ANCHICERATOPS?

Canadian dinosaur collector Charles M. Sternberg discovered what may have been another kind (species) of *Anchiceratops* in 1929. He named his discovery *Anchiceratops longirostris* (the long-snouted *Anchiceratops*). The new species had smaller horns and a longer snout. As it and *Anchiceratops ornatus* seem to have lived alongside each other, perhaps they were males and females of the same species.

Anchiceratops
(ANG-ki-SER-ah-tops)

 NAME: *Anchiceratops* means near to horn face
anchi (near to) + keratos (horn) + ops (face)

FAMILY: Ornithischian → Ceratopsian

SIZE: 15–20 ft (4.6–6 m) long; 6–7.5 ft (1.8–2.25 m) high at the hip

WEIGHT: 2–3 tons (1.8–2.7 tonnes)—about the same as 2–3 North American bison

 **FOOD:** plants

HABITAT: lowland coastal floodplains

WHERE: remains found in Canada

▶ *Anchiceratops*'s frill made up half the length of its complete skull.

WHEN: 80–70 million years ago in the Cretaceous period

		ANCHICERATOPS
TRIASSIC	JURASSIC	CRETACEOUS
250 MILLION YEARS AGO	205 MILLION YEARS AGO	135 MILLION YEARS AGO	65 MILLION YEARS AGO

How did *Anchiceratops* live?

As an ornithischian dinosaur, *Anchiceratops* ate plants. It bit through stems with its beak and chewed them up with its cheek teeth. Like other ceratopsians, it may have lived and traveled in herds. *Anchiceratops* roamed across a wide range of habitats, from wetland cypress swamps to dry evergreen woodlands.

◀ *Anchiceratops* had two long horns above its eyes, a large nose horn, and a tall frill topped with small hornlets.

Anchiceratops would probably have used its frill only for display in mating contests. Its horns may have been used for fighting or defense. Most of the big predators, such as *Albertosaurus*, would usually have left *Anchiceratops* alone. Even the largest predators would have found a healthy *Anchiceratops* a dangerous meal.

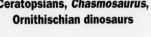
CHECK THESE OUT!

Albertosaurus, Centrosaurus, Ceratopsians, Chasmosaurus, Ornithischian dinosaurs

Anchisaurus

Prosauropods (early long-necked plant-eaters) were very common in the Late Triassic period, and some of them managed to live on into the Early Jurassic period. *Anchisaurus* was one of these survivors.

Anchisaurus was a prosauropod from the Jurassic period. It was very like *Thecodontosaurus* from the Late Triassic period, some 20 million years earlier. It is called a primitive prosauropod because it has not evolved much. For *Anchisaurus*, this means that its body, skull, and teeth were more like those we would expect to find in the earliest prosauropods.

Like its ancestors

The ancestors of *Anchisaurus* and other prosauropods lived in the Middle to Late Triassic period and were some of the very first dinosaurs. All dinosaurs evolved from a small, meat-eating animal that walked and ran on its long back legs, and looked a bit like *Eoraptor*.

FOOTPRINTS IN THE MUD

The broad, flat valley floors where *Anchisaurus* lived had many shallow lakes and ponds. The mud and sand around these stretches of water would have become covered in the footprints of dinosaurs and other animals that came to drink. These footprints fossilized because during the Early Jurassic period it seems that Massachusetts and Connecticut had two seasons: dry and wet.

During the dry seasons, the water in the lakes and ponds would dry out, or evaporate. As the lakes got lower and lower, broad stretches of almost dry mud would be exposed to the air. Dinosaurs like *Anchisaurus* would have walked across these mudflats to get water to drink or to move to new feeding grounds. Eventually, the muddy ponds would dry out completely, leaving molded clay footprints. When it rained again, more mud would be washed down to cover and preserve the footprints.

We can see this ancestry clearly in *Anchisaurus* because its back legs are a good bit longer than its front legs. Most likely

▶ At about 8 ft (2.4 m) long, *Anchisaurus* was fairly small for a prosauropod.

DINOFACTS

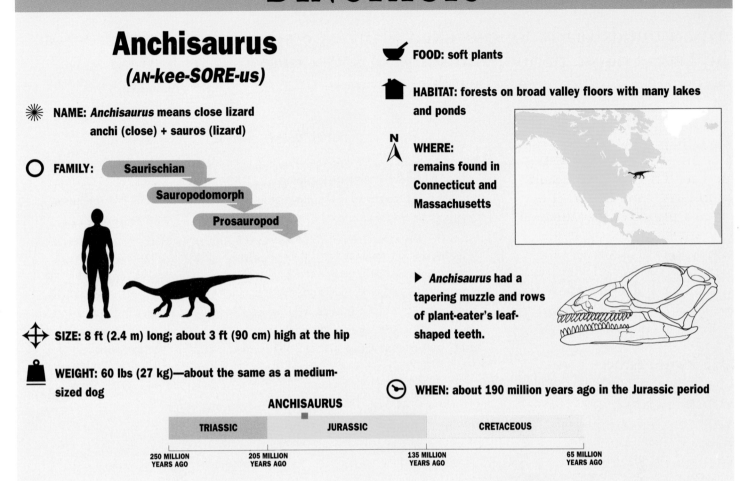

Anchisaurus
(AN-kee-SORE-us)

☀ **NAME:** *Anchisaurus* means close lizard
anchi (close) + sauros (lizard)

○ **FAMILY:** Saurischian → Sauropodomorph → Prosauropod

✛ **SIZE:** 8 ft (2.4 m) long; about 3 ft (90 cm) high at the hip

⬛ **WEIGHT:** 60 lbs (27 kg)—about the same as a medium-sized dog

🥣 **FOOD:** soft plants

🏠 **HABITAT:** forests on broad valley floors with many lakes and ponds

N ↑ **WHERE:** remains found in Connecticut and Massachusetts

▶ *Anchisaurus* had a tapering muzzle and rows of plant-eater's leaf-shaped teeth.

🕐 **WHEN:** about 190 million years ago in the Jurassic period

ANCHISAURUS

TRIASSIC	JURASSIC	CRETACEOUS
250 MILLION YEARS AGO / 205 MILLION YEARS AGO	135 MILLION YEARS AGO	65 MILLION YEARS AGO

Anchisaurus was able to run on its hind legs, like *Eoraptor*. It could also have walked on all four legs sometimes.

Because *Anchisaurus* had a very long back and a long neck, it would have been difficult for this dinosaur to keep its balance on just two legs when moving slowly. Think how much easier it is to balance on a bicycle when it is traveling quickly than when it is rolling very slowly. It is probable that the same principle of balance applied to prosauropods like *Anchisaurus*.

How did *Anchisaurus* live?
As a prosauropod, *Anchisaurus* would have eaten plants, but what kind? Scientists can make a few guesses. The fossils of *Anchisaurus* were found in sandstones and mudstones that were deposited in broad, flat valleys. These valleys appear to have had many lakes and ponds. Because of all the water, it seems likely that the plants in these valleys would have had softer, moister leaves than plants found in drier areas. The teeth of *Anchisaurus* do not appear to have been adapted for eating tough leaves and twigs. So it seems likely *Anchisaurus* would have eaten only soft leaves and stems.

CHECK THESE OUT!

Eoraptor, Footprints, Jurassic period, Prosauropods, Sauropodomorph dinosaurs, Triassic period

Ankylosaurs

The ankylosaurs (armored dinosaurs) were plant-eaters of the Jurassic and Cretaceous periods. Although they lived with many meat-eaters, they were protected by their bony armor and massive tail-clubs.

The ankylosaurs (armored dinosaurs) were tanklike plant-eaters that lived in many parts of the world. Paleontologists divide most of them into two groups—the ankylosaurids (named for *Ankylosaurus*), which had bony clubs at the tips of their tails, and the nodosaurids (named for *Nodosaurus*), which had no tail-clubs. All the ankylosaurids lived in the Late Cretaceous, while nodosaurids lived

NO WAY OUT

Fossils of club-tailed ankylosaurs (ankylosaurids) are found only in western North America and in China and Mongolia. Why are ankylosaurid remains never found in eastern North America or in western parts of Asia?

During the Late Cretaceous period, when the ankylosaurids were alive, a large, shallow sea covered the middle of the North American continent. Animals in western North America could not easily cross this sea to go east. Nor could eastern Asian animals move west very easily because of many high mountain ranges.

However, between the North American sea and the Asian mountains, a land bridge linked the North American and Asian continents. Asian animals could move east into North America and North American animals could move west into Asia. Today water covers this ancient land bridge and separates the two continents.

▶ *Euoplocephalus* (an ankylosaurid) and *Edmontonia* (a nodosaurid) visit a waterhole in Late Cretaceous Montana.

Euoplocephalus

Edmontonia

DINOFACTS

Ankylosaurs
(an-KY-lo-SORES)

HABITAT: forests

WHERE: remains found in North America, Asia, Europe, Australia, and possibly South America and Antarctica

NAME: Ankylosaur means fused lizard
ankylo (fused) + sauros (lizard)

FAMILY: Ornithischian
Thyreophoran

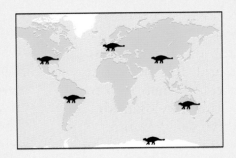

SIZE: 6.5–33 ft (2–10 m) long; 1–10 ft (30 cm–3 m) high at the hip

WEIGHT: up to 4 tons (3.6 tonnes)—about the same as 4 North American bison

FOOD: plants

WHEN: from about 185 million years ago in the Jurassic period to 65 million years ago in the Cretaceous period

ANKYLOSAURS

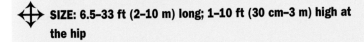

TRIASSIC	JURASSIC	CRETACEOUS
250 MILLION YEARS AGO	205 MILLION YEARS AGO	135 MILLION YEARS AGO	65 MILLION YEARS AGO

throughout the Cretaceous, and two kinds lived in the earlier Jurassic period. It is possible that the ankylosaurids evolved from the nodosaurids.

Two kinds of ankylosaurs, however, do not fit in either of these groups. *Minmi*, from Australia, and *Polacanthus*, from England and possibly North America, have features of both ankylosaurids and nodosaurids.

Living tanks
The ankylosaurs' armor was formed of bony plates, or osteoderms, growing in their skins. These large plates covered their heads, backs, parts of their tails, and the ankylosaurids' tail-clubs. The two pairs of osteoderms at the end of the tail grew into egg-shaped lumps fused to each other to form a solid structure.

To swing their clubs, ankylosaurids had very large tail muscles. Ankylosaurids shared their North American and Asian homes with the gigantic tyrannosaurs (two-fingered meat-eaters), so their tail-clubs would have been useful for defense.

How did ankylosaurs live?
As ornithischians (bird-hipped dinosaurs), ankylosaurs ate plants. Their skulls were very wide, and they had a turtle-like beak covering their snouts. Their bulky bodies probably housed large colonies of gut bacteria to help them to digest the large quantities of plants they ate each day.

CHECK THESE OUT!

Ankylosaurus, Cretaceous period, *Edmontonia, Euoplocephalus*, Hadrosaurs, *Minmi, Nodosaurus, Panoplosaurus, Pinacosaurus, Polacanthus, Saichania, Sauropelta*, Stegosaurs, *Talarurus, Tarchia*, Thyreophorans, Tyrannosaurs

Ankylosaurus

Ankylosaurus was a large plant-eating dinosaur that must have looked like a walking mountain. It gave its name to the ankylosaur group of dinosaurs, just as the tyrannosaurs are named for *Tyrannosaurus*.

Ankylosaurus was described by American paleontologist Barnum Brown in 1908. *Ankylosaurus* was among the last of the nonflying dinosaurs; it lived during the last two or three million years of the Cretaceous period.

How did *Ankylosaurus* live?
Paleontologists can tell from the shape of *Ankylosaurus*'s bones that it was well adapted

MYSTERIOUS CAVITIES

Like the first archosaurs, the ankylosaurs had many openings in the fronts of their skulls. Most animals have small chambers in their snouts that help them smell. Mammals, however, have greatly enlarged openings. This is because the sense of smell is very important for mammals. They also need to warm the air before they breathe it into their lungs. If a warm-bodied mammal were to breathe cold air deep into its lungs, it would chill its body too much.

Scientists are not sure why ankylosaurs had so many chambers in their snouts. What did they use them for? Was it so that they could smell certain plants and tell if they were edible? Were these dinosaurs warm-blooded, so that they needed to warm up the air before breathing it in? No one knows for sure.

◀ Mighty but slow-moving *Ankylosaurus* had so much armor it had no need to fear attack from hungry predators like the tyrannosaurs.

for a slow pace of life. The patterns of marks where muscles attached to bones show that although *Ankylosaurus*'s muscles were positioned to provide great force, they would have moved its legs and arms very slowly.

With its huge body, *Ankylosaurus* did not have to worry about being attacked. Adult elephants in Africa today are rarely attacked by lions—the largest predators there. In case *Ankylosaurus* ever did feel threatened, it had bony plates covering its neck, back, and the base of its tail.

Ankylosaurus also had a bony club at the end of its tail. *Ankylosaurus*'s strong tail muscles let it swing its clubbed tail quickly like a hammer. This would have been helpful as *Ankylosaurus* lived with the fierce predator *Tyrannosaurus*. *Ankylosaurus* gave its name to two groups of dinosaurs: ankylosaurs (armored dinosaurs) and ankylosaurids, armored dinosaurs that had tail–clubs.

Ankylosaurus had a beak at the front of its mouth to help bite and cut plants. *Ankylosaurus* also had cheeks. So it must have chewed its food a little. However, since its teeth were tiny and found only on the sides of its jaw, it probably ate only soft foods, and did not chew them very much.

CHECK THESE OUT!

Ankylosaurs, Archosaurs, Cretaceous period, Thyreophorans, Tyrannosaurs, *Tyrannosaurus*

DINOFACTS

Ankylosaurus
(an-KY-lo-SORE-us)

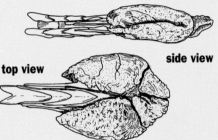

top view / side view

▶ *Ankylosaurus*'s tail-club was made of big bony plates fused to the bones at the end of the tail. It was swung from side to side by the strong muscles in the tail and could give a powerful blow.

✳ **NAME:** *Ankylosaurus* means fused lizard
ankylo (fused) + sauros (lizard)

○ **FAMILY:**   Ornithischian

Thyreophoran

Ankylosaur

✛ **SIZE:** 33 ft (10 m) long; about 10 ft (3 m) high at the hip

WEIGHT: 4 tons (3.6 tonnes)—about the same as 4 North American bison

FOOD: plants

HABITAT: moist forests

WHERE: remains found in Montana and Wyoming, and in Alberta, Canada

🕐 **WHEN:** about 68–65 million years ago in the Cretaceous period

ANKYLOSAURS

TRIASSIC	JURASSIC	CRETACEOUS
250 MILLION YEARS AGO	205 MILLION YEARS AGO	135 MILLION YEARS AGO	65 MILLION YEARS AGO

Antarctosaurus

Antarctosaurus was a sauropod (long-necked plant-eater) that lived in South America in the Late Cretaceous period. Paleontologists know it was a big dinosaur, but they do not know just how big.

Of all the Cretaceous sauropods that lived in South America, *Antarctosaurus* seems to have been one of the most widespread. Fossil-hunters have found its remains scattered across four South American countries.

Plant-eating titans

Antarctosaurus belonged to the group of armored sauropods called the titanosaurs. The titanosaurs lived mainly south of the equator in the Cretaceous period, when the northern sauropods, such as *Diplodocus* and its relatives, had died out. Some paleontologists believe that most titanosaurs, like *Saltasaurus*, had armor, although no armor has yet been found for *Antarctosaurus*.

The best specimen of *Antarctosaurus* was an incomplete skeleton found in Argentina. German paleontologist F. von Huene described these remains in 1929. The fossils included parts of the skull that covered the

BITS AND PIECES

When an animal dies in the wild, other animals gather to eat its carcass. These scavengers may pull off pieces and drag them away, spreading bones all over the place. Dinosaurs probably acted the same way, which is why paleontologists often do not recover whole skeletons. Scavengers are not paleontologists' only problem. If a dinosaur's dead body fell into a river, the currents in the river would break it up and scatter it. Also, the flowing water could mix together different bones from several very decayed animals. Sometimes paleontologists cannot tell whether the bones they are studying belong to one, two, or more animals.

Antarctosaurus's bones were just scattered shards. The pieces may belong to more than one type of animal. The ankle bones do not resemble the ankle bones of any other known sauropod. Scientists really need better specimens before they can be sure what *Antarctosaurus* was like.

▶ Like other sauropods, *Antarctosaurus* could have used its long neck to browse on leaves and stems high up in trees.

48

brain, part of the lower jaw with teeth, a single bit of neck bone, a shoulder blade, some bones from one arm and one leg, and part of the hip.

Antarctosaurus's back and tail bones were not found, so paleontologists do not have a good idea of how long its body would have been. However, scientists found enough arm and leg bones to get a good idea of what its limbs were like. Their size shows that *Antarctosaurus* was a very large animal. Because *Antarctosaurus* also had fairly slim leg and arm bones, this large sauropod was probably not as heavy as others of the same size.

How it lived

Antarctosaurus's teeth show that it ate plants, like all sauropods. *Antarctosaurus* may have lived in small herds as well. Paleontologists think that some kinds of sauropods lived in herds because they have found sauropod trackways that show small groups moving in the same direction. However, scientists have not yet found a group trackway specifically for *Antarctosaurus*.

CHECK THESE OUT!

Cretaceous period, *Diplodocus*, *Saltasaurus*, Saurischian dinosaurs, Sauropods, *Titanosaurus*

DINOFACTS

Antarctosaurus
(ant-ARK-tuh-SORE-us)

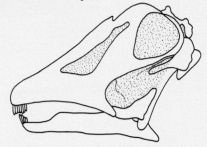

▶ Like all sauropods, *Antarctosaurus* had a small skull for its body size. Like *Diplodocus*, it had peglike teeth only at the front of its mouth.

✳ **NAME:** *Antarctosaurus* means Antarctic lizard
antarctos (Antarctic) + sauros (lizard)

⬤ **FAMILY:**

Saurischian → Sauropodomorph → Sauropod

✥ **SIZE:** perhaps 66–100 ft (20–30 m) long; perhaps 14 ft (4.3 m) high at the hip

⬛ **WEIGHT:** about 20–30 tons (18–27.2 tonnes)—about the same as 4–6 African elephants

FOOD: plants

HABITAT: broad, forested river valleys

WHERE: remains found in Argentina, Brazil, Chile, and Uruguay

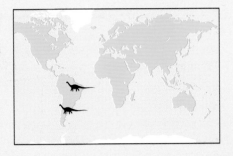

🕐 **WHEN:** about 80–65 million years ago in the Cretaceous period

			ANTARCTOSAURUS
TRIASSIC	JURASSIC	CRETACEOUS	
250 MILLION YEARS AGO	205 MILLION YEARS AGO	135 MILLION YEARS AGO	65 MILLION YEARS AGO

Apatosaurus

Apatosaurus is one of the most famous dinosaurs in the world, but most people know it by its old name, *Brontosaurus*. This large sauropod (long-necked plant-eater) lived in the Jurassic period.

In 1883, US paleontologist Othniel C. Marsh published the first complete reconstruction of a sauropod. He called it *Brontosaurus*. Unfortunately he used the leg bones and skull of *Camarasaurus*, which gave a false picture of the new dinosaur.

Only later did paleontologists realize that *Brontosaurus* was the same as *Apatosaurus*, a sauropod that Marsh had named in 1877. Because the name *Apatosaurus* had been used first, the name *Brontosaurus* is no longer used.

Diplodocus cousin

Apatosaurus was one of the diplodocid sauropods (closely related to *Diplodocus*). Like other diplodocids it had long, thin, pencil-like teeth crowded

▶ **Like other diplodocid sauropods, *Apatosaurus* had a slender-tipped tail that it may have cracked like a whip to scare predators.**

together at the front of its mouth, and a long, low head.

Apatosaurus was not as long as *Diplodocus*, but its bones were much thicker and stronger. Shorter, stockier *Apatosaurus* must have weighed more than the taller, leaner *Diplodocus*. Some of *Apatosaurus*'s backbones that

lay between its hipbones were fused. This seems to have strengthened the animal's back.

Some paleontologists have suggested that diplodocids could raise themselves on to their hind legs to feed on taller trees. The strengthening of the backbones at the hips could have helped *Apatosaurus* to support its huge weight on its hind legs.

LIVING TOGETHER

The Late Jurassic rocks of the western United States have produced several different kinds of large sauropods. These different kinds appear to have lived at roughly the same time. There would have been a great struggle for all these large animals to get enough to eat—or would there?

When several kinds of animals share a habitat for a long time, they gradually evolve features that prevent their ways of life from being too similar. If closely related, but slightly different, animals eat different foods, they can all find food to eat in the same habitat. This way many more different types of animals can live together in the same habitat.

It seems that the different types of sauropods found ways to share their Jurassic habitat. Different sized sauropods would have eaten leaves and twigs from different heights. Different types of teeth in different sauropods suggest that each species also ate slightly different types of plants or parts of plants.

How did *Apatosaurus* live?

Fossil trackways show that *Apatosaurus* may have lived in small groups. The trackways show a small number of *Apatosaurus*, not more than about 20 animals, moving together in a single direction.

A group of large plant-eating *Apatosaurus* would soon eat all the plants in a particular area. These dinosaurs must have had to move from place to place to find enough to eat.

Whiplash tails

Apatosaurus's tail had a long, thin tip. In 1997 some scientists suggested that *Apatosaurus* could have cracked its tail like a gigantic whip to scare off attackers, threaten others of its own kind, or attract mates. However, such behavior could have hurt too much to do regularly.

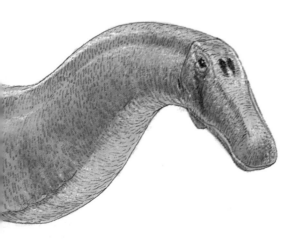

CHECK THESE OUT!

Camarasaurus, Collecting dinosaurs, *Diplodocus*, Footprints, Jurassic period, Sauropods

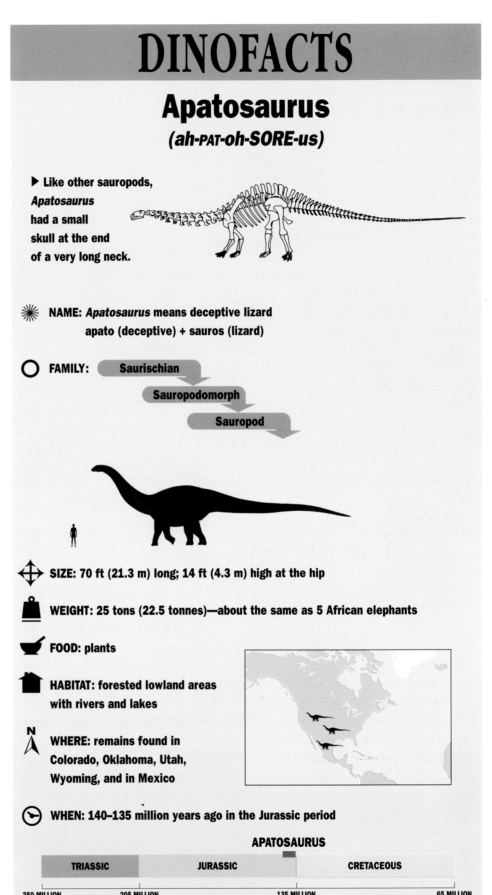

DINOFACTS

Apatosaurus
(ah-PAT-oh-SORE-us)

▶ Like other sauropods, *Apatosaurus* had a small skull at the end of a very long neck.

✳ **NAME:** *Apatosaurus* means deceptive lizard
apato (deceptive) + sauros (lizard)

○ **FAMILY:** Saurischian

Sauropodomorph

Sauropod

✛ **SIZE:** 70 ft (21.3 m) long; 14 ft (4.3 m) high at the hip

⚖ **WEIGHT:** 25 tons (22.5 tonnes)—about the same as 5 African elephants

🥣 **FOOD:** plants

🏠 **HABITAT:** forested lowland areas with rivers and lakes

N **WHERE:** remains found in Colorado, Oklahoma, Utah, Wyoming, and in Mexico

🕐 **WHEN:** 140–135 million years ago in the Jurassic period

		APATOSAURUS	
TRIASSIC	JURASSIC		CRETACEOUS
250 MILLION YEARS AGO	205 MILLION YEARS AGO	135 MILLION YEARS AGO	65 MILLION YEARS AGO

Archaeopteryx

Archaeopteryx lived in Germany in the Late Jurassic period and was an amazing dinosaur. It was an avialan, a close relative of modern birds. It had feathers and a beak, and it could fly.

The very first *Archaeopteryx* skeleton was found in 1861, just two years after the publication of Charles Darwin's book *On the Origin of Species*, in which Darwin explained his theory of evolution. This theory is now widely accepted, but at that time it was not. The discovery of *Archaeopteryx*, which was halfway between a dinosaur and a modern bird, was important in persuading many people to accept the idea of evolution.

The first hint that anything like *Archaeopteryx* existed was the discovery in 1861 of a single feather in the Solnhofen quarry in Germany. Since then, fossil-hunters have

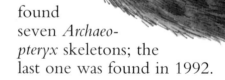

▶ *Archaeopteryx* takes to the air. It may not have been as good at flying as modern birds, and it may have needed its long tail to help it stay level.

found seven *Archaeopteryx* skeletons; the last one was found in 1992.

LEARNING TO FLY

Did *Archaeopteryx*'s ancestors first fly by gliding down from trees, or by running really fast on the ground and sticking out their feathery wings? Some paleontologists ask how a two-legged dinosaur could get to the top of a tree in the first place? Also, how could it balance on branches if it did not have the gripping feet of modern birds?

Perhaps, then, *Archaeopteryx*'s ancestors first flew, not from a tree, but from the ground. Perhaps the ancestors of *Archaeopteryx* were fast-running, ground-living animals. The feathers on their wings may have been used to help the animals catch their food, or for display to signal to others of their own kind (species). As these animals ran along the ground, they could have stuck out their feathered arms. The speed of the animal, combined with the air flowing over the wings, may have allowed these running dinosaurs to glide a little bit off the ground. The animals may have eventually discovered that by flapping their arms they could stay in the air, covering greater distances. Over many generations, animals could have evolved with the feathered wings that we see in *Archaeopteryx*.

Bird relatives

So what kind of animal was *Archaeopteryx*? *Archaeopteryx* was the earliest known avialan. The avialans are a group of dinosaurs that include birds and their closest relatives.

Avialans belong to a larger groups of dinosaurs called the maniraptors (long-armed dinosaurs). Other maniraptors include the dromaeosaurs

(clawed meat-eaters) such as *Dromaeo-saurus* and *Deinonychus*. Dromaeosaurs were close relatives of *Archaeopteryx* and the avialans, and shared several features with them. For example, both dromaeo-saurs and avialans had special wrist bones that let them fold their hands away as they ran. Also, in the hips of most saurischian (lizard-hipped) dinosaurs, the pubis sticks out forward and down from the hip socket. However, in *Dromaeosaurus* and *Deinonychus*, the pubis pointed straight down. In *Archaeopteryx*, it even pointed slightly backward as it does in modern birds.

Turning tail

The tails of *Dromaeosaurus* and *Deinonychus* were different from other dinosaurs' tails, too. They were stiffened with bony rods, and paleontologists think dromaeosaurs used them to turn quickly while running. Modern flying birds use their tails to turn in the air. The only difference is that birds' tails are not bony rods but stiff tail feathers controlled by muscles. *Archaeo-pteryx*'s long, feathered tail is the perfect halfway point between the short, stiff, feathered tail of modern birds and the long, stiff, unfeathered tail of the dromaeosaurs.

Feathered fossil

The most important feature of *Archaeopteryx* is its feathers. Not only did *Archaeopteryx* have feathers like a bird, but the feathers on its arms were shaped exactly like the feathers of modern flying birds.

All feathers have a central rod (shaft) with soft, flexible bristles (vanes) on either side. In flying birds, the wing feather vanes are wider on one side of the shaft than on the other. *Archaeopteryx*'s wing feathers were shaped the same way. Even under a micro-scope, *Archaeopteryx*'s feathers look like modern bird feathers.

The feathers of birds and the scales of lizards and snakes are not all that different. Both start out as little bumps in the upper layers of the skin, and both are made from fingernail-like material called keratin. If you look at a bird's foot, you will see that the skin looks like the scales on a lizard's foot.

Why feathers?

Paleontologists wonder why *Archaeopteryx*'s ancestors would have had feathers even though

they did not fly. Some paleontologists think that the feathers trapped in the dinosaurs' body heat and stopped them from getting cold. Others believe that feathers kept sunlight off the dinosaurs' skin and stopped them from overheating.

Whichever explanation is correct, at some time these animals would have discovered that the feathers on their arms allowed them to glide a little through the air. Over millions of years, animals would have evolved with the wings and flight muscles that we see in *Archaeopteryx*.

Although *Archaeopteryx*'s feathers indicate that it could fly, its chest bones were not as strongly built as those of later flying avialans and modern flying birds. These all have a

big, deep, flat breastbone running down the front of their chests to which their powerful flight muscles attach.

▲ A flying squirrel spreads the flaps of skin between its arms and legs and leaps from the treetops. Perhaps *Archaeopteryx* flew something like this.

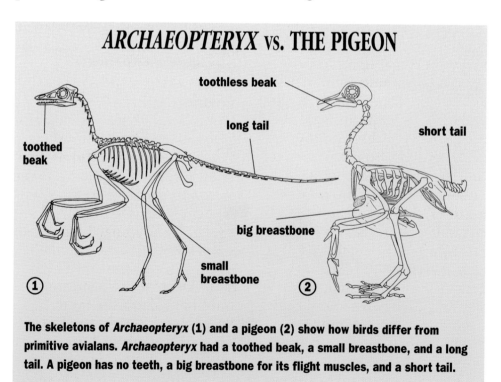

ARCHAEOPTERYX vs. THE PIGEON

toothless beak

long tail

short tail

toothed beak

big breastbone

small breastbone

① ②

The skeletons of *Archaeopteryx* (1) and a pigeon (2) show how birds differ from primitive avialans. *Archaeopteryx* had a toothed beak, a small breastbone, and a long tail. A pigeon has no teeth, a big breastbone for its flight muscles, and a short tail.

Birds also have a large wishbone, which helps them to flap their wings. When the flight muscles pull the wings down, the wishbone pushes the wings back up again ready for the next downstroke. *Archaeopteryx* did not have a big breastbone and had only a small wishbone. *Archaeopteryx* could probably flap its wings weakly, but it would not have been a powerful flier.

How *Archaeopteryx* lived

Some paleontologists think that *Archaeopteryx* clambered around in trees, searching for insects to eat. The claws on its fingers would have helped it to climb.

These claws are very similar to the wing claws of young hoatzins. The hoatzin is a tropical South American bird, and its young use their wing claws to help them climb.

Being able to climb trees could also explain how *Archaeopteryx*, or its ancestors, first came to fly. Several kinds (species) of gliding frogs, lizards, and mammals live in trees today. These animals can all form broad, flat surfaces that enable them to jump from the trees and glide through the air.

The gliding frogs have extra-wide hands and feet with webbing between the fingers and toes. The lizards can spread out their ribs to form a flat surface. The mammals, such as flying squirrels, have flaps of skin along their sides that join their arms and legs.

All these gliding animals climb up trees, jump off branches, and glide down to the branches or trunks of other trees. *Archaeopteryx*'s ancestors could have done the same, except that instead of just skin they had feathers to form the surface for gliding. However, there is no way to tell for sure.

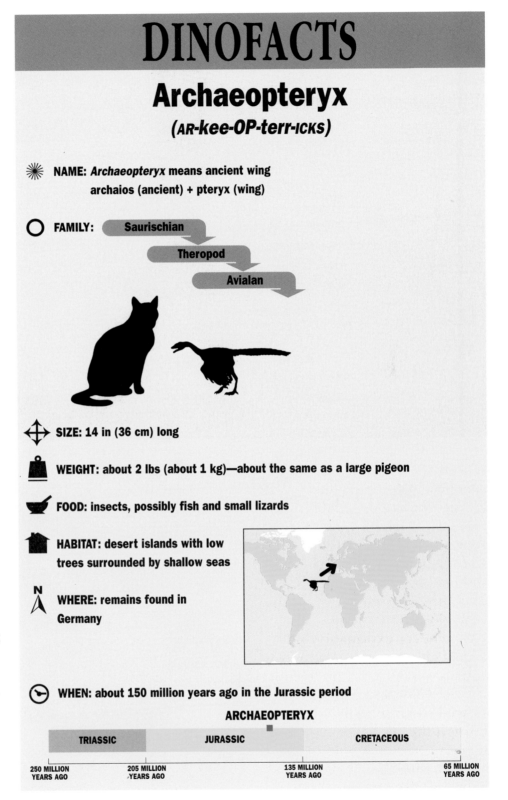

DINOFACTS

Archaeopteryx
(AR-kee-OP-terr-ICKS)

NAME: *Archaeopteryx* means ancient wing
archaios (ancient) + pteryx (wing)

FAMILY: Saurischian → Theropod → Avialan

SIZE: 14 in (36 cm) long

WEIGHT: about 2 lbs (about 1 kg)—about the same as a large pigeon

FOOD: insects, possibly fish and small lizards

HABITAT: desert islands with low trees surrounded by shallow seas

WHERE: remains found in Germany

WHEN: about 150 million years ago in the Jurassic period

ARCHAEOPTERYX

TRIASSIC	JURASSIC	CRETACEOUS
250 MILLION YEARS AGO	205 MILLION YEARS AGO	135 MILLION YEARS AGO · 65 MILLION YEARS AGO

CHECK THESE OUT!

Avialans, Birds, *Deinonychus,*
Dromaeosaurs, *Dromaeosaurus,*
Jurassic period, Saurischian dinosaurs

Archosaurs

The archosaurs, or ruling lizards, appeared at the boundary between the Permian and Triassic periods, some 250 million years ago. They evolved into the pterosaurs, the crocodiles, and the dinosaurs.

Soon after the largest known extinction, about 250 million years ago, a group of small, meat-eating animals started to evolve into a wide variety of running and flying animals—the archosaurs, the ruling reptiles or lizards. The Mesozoic dinosaurs were the most famous members of this group, but archosaurs are still with us today. We call them crocodiles and birds.

The archosaurs, with the lepidosaurs (scaly reptiles like lizards, snakes, and the tuatara), make up the group of egg-laying animals known as diapsids. Diapsids have two pairs of openings in their skulls behind their eye sockets.

Holes in the head

Archosaurs differ from lepidosaurs in two important ways. The most obvious difference is in their skulls. Besides having openings behind the eye sockets, archosaurs also have a large opening on either side of the skull in front of the eye sockets. Lepidosaurs do not have these extra openings.

Most archosaurs also tend to hold their limbs more upright than lepidosaurs. Their hip and shoulder sockets open more downward instead of sideways as they do in

lizards. When most archosaurs walk, their limbs are held beneath the body. In lepidosaurs, the arms and legs stick out to the sides, and the hands and feet swing out far from the body as the animals move. Having the legs held beneath the body made it easier for the leg muscles of archosaurs to support it. Dinosaurs were archosaurs, and they could never have grown as big as they did if they had not had the archosaur type of legs, hips, and shoulders.

Rulers of the land and air

In the Triassic period, archosaurs evolved many different body forms and lived in many different habitats. Dinosaurs were just one of many

archosaur groups, but they were the most successful. The dinosaurs were the ruling large land animals in the Jurassic and Cretaceous periods.

Archosaurs also evolved flapping flight twice: once as pterosaurs, and again as avialans (birds and their closest relatives). During the Triassic, Jurassic, and Early Cretaceous periods, the pterosaurs were the ruling large flying animals. In the Late Cretaceous period, modern birds took over.

AIR HEADS

The most recognizable feature of archosaurs is the large opening on either side of the skull just in front of the eyes. What did these extra openings do? Perhaps they made the skull lighter without making it any weaker. The snout of the skull was strong enough by itself, and the area around the eyes was also solidly braced.

Perhaps when the archosaurs evolved, most of the world's land was hot and dry. There would not have been a lot of fresh water around for the animals to drink. To get rid of excess salt in their bodies, the archosaurs may have evolved with skull openings to fit special salt-removing glands. Modern seabirds have such glands.

However, many scientists believe the holes held hot air. Many birds and crocodiles also have air vents in their skulls that help them keep a cool head. Scientists think that the extra space near the snout may improve the sense of smell, while space at the back of the skull might improve hearing.

▼ Two *Saurosuchus* spar in Triassic Argentina. *Saurosuchus* was a huge, crocodile-like archosaur and the fiercest land predator of its time.

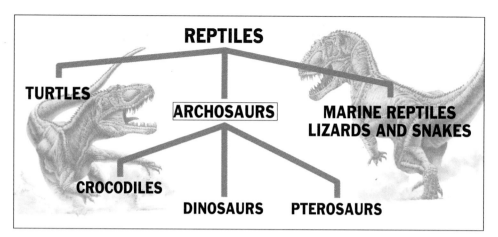

REPTILES

TURTLES

ARCHOSAURS

MARINE REPTILES
LIZARDS AND SNAKES

CROCODILES

DINOSAURS   PTEROSAURS

◀ The archosaurs contain the crocodiles, the pterosaurs, and the dinosaurs. Like marine reptiles, lizards, and snakes, archosaurs are diapsid reptiles. Turtles are anapsids, with no hole in the skull behind the eye sockets.

Early archosaurs

The earliest known archosaur was *Archosaurus*, which lived in Russia about 260 million years ago in the Permian period. *Archosaurus* hunted and ate meat or fish, like most of the early archosaurs.

Archosaurus would have lived like modern crocodiles. Its legs would have sprawled out to the sides, and it would have had the same numbers of holes in its skull as all later diapsid archosaurs. Fossils of close relatives of *Archosaurus* have been discovered in rocks of Early Triassic age in South Africa and China.

South Africa also has very good fossils of an early land-living archosaur called *Euparkeria*. This animal was about 2 ft (60 cm) long and had a large skull with long, sharp teeth. Some paleontologists think that *Euparkeria* could run quickly on its long hind legs, just as the collared lizard of the western United States does today.

Big archosaurs

The first large archosaur fossils also come from Early Triassic rocks of South Africa and China. These big archosaurs were the erythrosuchians, or crimson crocodiles. Their name comes from the red color of the rocks in which their fossils are found. Despite their name, these were not true crocodiles but only crocodile-like. Their wrists, hips, shoulders, and skulls were slightly different from those of true crocodiles, which first appeared in the Jurassic period.

Erythrosuchians must have been very dangerous hunters. One of them, *Erythrosuchus*, had a skull about 3 ft (90 cm) long! Its total length was almost 16 ft (5 m), and its jaws were lined with long, sharp teeth. *Erythrosuchus* could grow to a large size because its limbs had taken on a more vertical position under its body.

Paleontologists recognize *Erythrosuchus* as the first case of the evolution of large body size in archosaurs. The dinosaurs continued this

▼ *Petrolacosaurus* (1) was the earliest known diapsid reptile and the ancestor of the archosaurs. It had openings behind the eye sockets but not in front. It lived in Kansas in the Carboniferous period (360–290 million years ago). *Euparkeria* (2) was a diapsid archosaur that lived in South Africa in the Triassic period. It had openings behind and in front of the eyes.

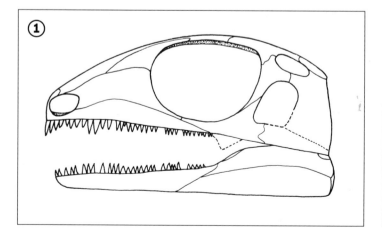

①

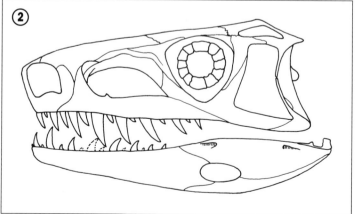

②

evolution of large bodies tens of millions of years later, eventually giving rise to the giant sauropods (long-necked plant-eaters), such as *Apatosaurus* and *Brachiosaurus*.

Monster archosaurs
During most of the Triassic period, the archosaurs were the ruling meat-eaters. The rauisuchians were a worldwide group of fierce, running, meat-eating archosaurs. They would have looked a bit like long-legged crocodiles, but while most modern crocodile skulls are quite flat, rauisuchian skulls were narrow and deep.

This shape made the skulls of rauisuchians very strong. Because long roots anchored their long, serrated teeth firmly to their jaws, the rauisuchians could rip through the toughest hides. *Saurosuchus* (lizard crocodile) was a 27 ft (8.2 m) rauisuchian from Argentina that would have attacked and eaten just about any land animal it could catch.

In the lakes and rivers of the Triassic period, phytosaurs, or leaf lizards, were the most dangerous predators. They were distant relatives of crocodiles. They looked very similar to the modern gharial, a type of fish-eating crocodile. In crocodiles, the nostrils are at the tip of the snout; in phytosaurs, the nostrils were on a raised bump of bone just in front of the eyes.

Here come the dinosaurs!
While the rauisuchians were prowling the land and the phytosaurs were hunting the

waters, smaller meat-eating archosaurs, such as the ornithosuchids, or bird crocodiles (so named because they walked on two legs and had three-toed feet) also roamed. Ornithosuchid skeletons are very similar to dinosaur skeletons. Some scientists think they might be the ancestors of the dinosaurs. Others think the dinosaurs evolved from the lagosuchids, or lake crocodiles,

a group of small two-legged archosaurs. They lived in Argentina in the Middle Triassic period, just before the first dinosaurs, *Eoraptor* and *Herrerasaurus*, appeared.

CHECK THESE OUT!
Crocodiles, Dinosaurs, *Eoraptor*, *Herrerasaurus*, Pterosaurs, Reptiles, Triassic period

FOSSIL FACTS

Archosaurs
(ARE-keh-SORES)

 NAME: Archosaur means ruling lizard archo (ruler) + sauros (lizard)

 FAMILY: 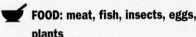 Reptile

SIZE: (including birds) huge variation from 2.3 in (5.8 cm) to 120 ft (37 m) or more long

 WEIGHT: (including birds) huge variation from 0.06 oz (1.6 g) to 50 tons (45 tonnes) or more—or from a bee hummingbird to 10 African elephants

 FOOD: meat, fish, insects, eggs, plants

HABITAT: all habitats, but only birds can live in the polar regions and temperate seas and oceans

N **WHERE:** remains found worldwide

WHEN: from 260 million years ago in the Permian period to today

ARCHOSAURS

DEVONIAN	CARBONIFEROUS	PERMIAN	TRIASSIC	JURASSIC	CRETACEOUS
410 MILLION YEARS AGO	360 MILLION YEARS AGO	290 MILLION YEARS AGO	250 MILLION YEARS AGO	205 MILLION YEARS AGO	135 MILLION YEARS AGO

65 MILLION YEARS AGO

Argentinosaurus

Argentinosaurus was a huge titanosaur that lived in Argentina in the Cretaceous period. The titanosaurs were armored sauropods (long-necked plant-eaters) that lived mainly south of the equator.

Most people interested in dinosaurs will have heard of the big Late Jurassic sauropods of western North America: animals such as *Brachiosaurus* and *Seismosaurus*. However, these animals were not alone in their great size. The titanosaur *Argentinosaurus* was a giant, but not of the Jurassic period; it lived later, in the Cretaceous period.

Argentine paleontologists José Bonaparte and Rodolfo Coria described *Argentinosaurus* in 1993. Unfortunately, they did not have a complete skeleton, only a few backbones, the tops of the hips, one piece of rib, and one lower leg bone. These pieces do, however, give a good idea of how big *Argentinosaurus* was.

Long bones

The lower leg bone of *Argentinosaurus* was 5 ft (1.5 m) long. Using the leg of another South American sauropod, *Patagosaurus*, as a model, scientists can estimate the total length of *Argentinosaurus*'s legs from the one bone they have found.

Based on *Patagosaurus*, they estimate that the upper leg bone of *Argentinosaurus* was between 7 ft and 8 ft (about 2.4 m) long. Adding on a bit for the length of the ankle and foot bones, scientists have

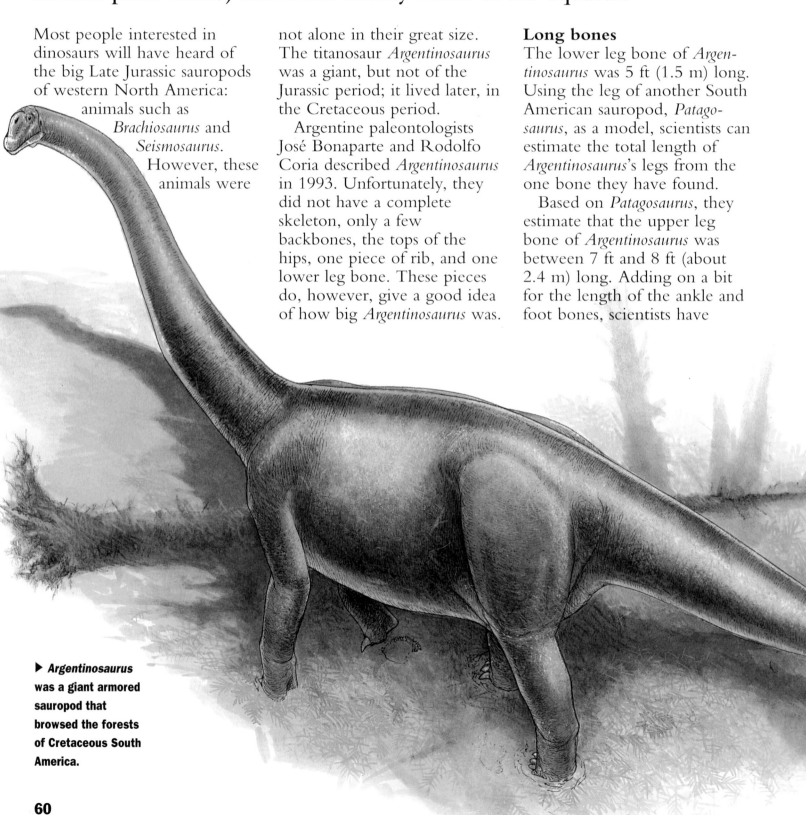

▶ *Argentinosaurus* was a giant armored sauropod that browsed the forests of Cretaceous South America.

worked out that *Argentinosaurus*'s leg was an astonishing 16 ft (5 m) long, compared with a leg length of about 14 ft (4.3 m) in *Brachiosaurus*. *Seismosaurus*'s leg length has not been estimated because no leg bones have been found.

How it lived

Argentinosaurus was a sauropod, so paleontologists know that it ate plants. However, because no teeth or pieces of jawbone have been found, they cannot tell what sorts of plants it ate. It probably browsed on leaves from the tallest trees, reaching up with its long neck.

LAND OF THE GIANTS

Cretaceous rocks in Patagonia have produced some giant dinosaurs. Besides *Argentinosaurus*, this region has produced the huge meat-eater *Giganotosaurus*, and *Megaraptor*, the largest claw-footed predator ever found. *Megaraptor* may be a dromaeosaur. Scientists are not sure.

The Late Jurassic rocks of western North America are the only other source of giant dinosaur fossils. These rocks are filled with giant sauropods like *Brachiosaurus*, *Supersaurus*, and *Seismosaurus*, and the huge, poorly known predators *Torvosaurus* and *Saurophaganax*. Both places were once dry floodplains with many evergreens. Perhaps this type of setting might have been particularly suitable for large sauropods, which in turn were food for very large predators.

Like *Saltasaurus*, another titanosaur, *Argentinosaurus* probably had small armor plates set in its skin. Fossil-hunters have not yet found any *Argentinosaurus* armor, though.

CHECK THESE OUT!

Brachiosaurus, Cretaceous period, *Patagosaurus*, *Saltasaurus*, Saurischian dinosaurs, *Titanosaurus*

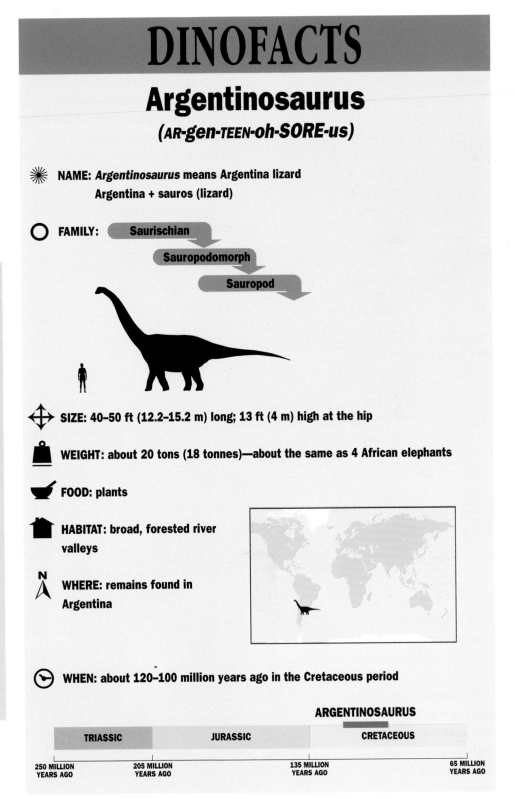

DINOFACTS

Argentinosaurus
(AR-gen-TEEN-oh-SORE-us)

✳ **NAME:** *Argentinosaurus* means Argentina lizard
Argentina + sauros (lizard)

○ **FAMILY:** Saurischian → Sauropodomorph → Sauropod

✛ **SIZE:** 40–50 ft (12.2–15.2 m) long; 13 ft (4 m) high at the hip

WEIGHT: about 20 tons (18 tonnes)—about the same as 4 African elephants

FOOD: plants

HABITAT: broad, forested river valleys

N **WHERE:** remains found in Argentina

🕐 **WHEN:** about 120–100 million years ago in the Cretaceous period

		ARGENTINOSAURUS
TRIASSIC	JURASSIC	CRETACEOUS
250 MILLION YEARS AGO	205 MILLION YEARS AGO	135 MILLION YEARS AGO ⸱ 65 MILLION YEARS AGO

Arrhinoceratops

The horned dinosaur *Arrhinoceratops* lived 75–70 million years ago. Because it was very similar to the later *Torosaurus*, some scientists think it may have been one of *Torosaurus*'s ancestors.

In 1923, fossil-hunters from the University of Toronto discovered a nearly complete skull of a ceratopsian (horned dinosaur) near the Red Deer River in Alberta, Canada. Two years later, Canadian paleontologist William Parks named this specimen *Arrhinoceratops*.

FIGHTING *ARRHINOCERATOPS*?

The only *Arrhinoceratops* skull that fossil-hunters have found had a hole in the left side of its frill. Similar holes have been found in the frills of other ceratopsians. Paleontologists have suggested that the holes were made by other horned dinosaurs. Perhaps as rams do today, these animals fought to decide who was boss. Maybe the dinosaurs first raised their big frills in display and made mock charges at each other, since most animals usually do not risk serious injury to show who is the stronger. If neither animal backed down, they probably fought, or shoved cheek to cheek.

▶ *Arrhinoceratops* roamed Canada at the same time as *Anchiceratops*, another ceratopsian. *Arrhinoceratops* had a broader, plainer frill and a shorter muzzle than its cousin did.

Paleontologists classify most ceratopsians into two major groups: the chasmosaurines and the centrosaurines. The chasmosaurines, named for *Chasmosaurus*, had long, bony frills at the back of their skulls. They also had long horns above their eyes and a short nose horn. The centrosaurines, named for *Centrosaurus*, had shorter frills, small eye horns, and large nose horns. *Arrhinoceratops* was a chasmosaurine ceratopsian.

Arrhinoceratops was unusual because the horns above its eyes curved outward more than those of most horned dinosaurs. Its face was also shorter than that of most chasmosaurines.

Arrhinoceratops's nose horn was short and thick. When William Parks studied *Arrhinoceratops*, he thought it had no nose horn. However, it seems that chasmosaurine nose horns were made up of a small bony core plus a separate bone that fused to the skull only in older animals. Parks's dinosaur was later found to have a small horn core, but no extra horn bone. Perhaps it was a young animal and the separate bone had fallen off and become lost after it died.

How *Arrhinoceratops* lived
Like all ceratopsians, *Arrhinoceratops* ate plants. It snipped off tough vegetation with its beak, sliced it up with its powerful jaws, and then digested it in its huge gut.

Arrhinoceratops shared its world with the tyrannosaur (two-fingered meat-eater)

DINOFACTS
Arrhinoceratops
(a-RYE-noh-SER-uh-tops)

☀ **NAME:** *Arrhinoceratops* means without nose horned face
a (without) + rhinos (nose) + keratos (horned) + ops (face)

○ **FAMILY:** Ornithischian

Ceratopsian

✛ **SIZE:** 20 ft (6 m) long; 8 ft (2.4 m) high at the hip

⬛ **WEIGHT:** 3 tons (2.7 tonnes)—about the same as 3 North American bison

FOOD: plants

🏠 **HABITAT:** lowland coastal floodplains

WHERE: remains found in Alberta, Canada

🕐 **WHEN:** 75–70 million years ago in the Cretaceous period

			ARRHINOCERATOPS
TRIASSIC	JURASSIC	CRETACEOUS	
250 MILLION YEARS AGO	205 MILLION YEARS AGO	135 MILLION YEARS AGO	65 MILLION YEARS AGO

Albertosaurus. However, only the largest *Albertosaurus* would have dared to attack this formidable dinosaur. Even then, it would have probably attacked only the old or weak.

CHECK THESE OUT!
Albertosaurus, Anchiceratops, Centrosaurus, Ceratopsians, Chasmosaurus, Torosaurus

Index

Page numbers in **bold** refer to main articles.